PRESENTS

THE DEFINITIVE
MANCHESTER UNITED
TRIVIA BOOK

Over 1,000 fascinating trivia questions, fun facts, stories and stats to test
and expand your knowledge of the Red Devils

BEAUTIFUL GAMES

Authors: Toby Everett & Anthony Tomas
Artwork: The Gucci Pirate

homeofbeautifulgames.com
@beautifulgamesco

Paperback ISBN: 978-1-7391976-1-2
Hardcover ISBN: 978-1-7391976-2-9

This book is dedicated to Charlie, Matilda, Asia, Holly, Valerie, Mark, Valentine and Kelly

TWO FREE BONUSES !

The most controversial Wold Cup moments ever
The most outragous Premier League moments ever

- What did Maradona really think of his infamous "Hand of God" goal?
- Why did Zidane headbutt Materazzi in a World Cup final?
- Why Eric Cantona hurled a Kung-Fu kick into the crowd?
- What made Paulo Di Canio push the refree onto the ground?
- Why a Columbian player was killed for scoring an own goal?

To find the answers scan the QR code and download your free copies

CONTENTS

INTRODUCTION

Welcome to the definitive Manchester United trivia book! This is more than just a collection of trivia questions, fun facts, stories, and stats. This book is a celebration of everything that makes Manchester United one of the greatest and most iconic clubs in world football.

This book is for everyone. Whether you're a diehard United supporter, a casual fan, or someone who is new to the club and eager to learn more. If you're belting your lungs out in the Stretford End of Old Trafford, screaming at the television in your living room or at the pub. If United is in your heart, this book will be your ultimate companion. You'll test and expand your knowledge of the Red Devils, settle debates with your mates and bask in the glory of the club's rich and storied history.

From its humble beginnings in 1878 as Newton Heath LYR (Lancashire & Yorkshire Railway), Manchester United has grown into a global phenomenon. However, It wasn't an easy journey to the top. If it wasn't for a chance meeting with a St Bernard dog called Major, the club wouldn't exist at all. The club has changed its name and stadium and survived unimaginable tragedy. But on the pitch, there have been triumphs that most clubs would envy. All of these have formed the soul of the club, which can be felt in every match.

Within these pages, you'll discover an array of fascinating trivia about the players, managers, trophies, transfers, and triumphs, mind-boggling records and statistics. This book also delves into the unique elements that make Manchester United so special and universally admired. You'll learn about the club's many kit sponsors, manufacturers, and badges that have adorned the iconic red shirt throughout the years. Famous starting line-ups that have taken to the pitch home and away. You'll immerse yourself in the passionate chants that have echoed through the stands for decades, creating an atmosphere like no other. You will relive the thrilling, nail-biting title races, memorable domestic cup runs and the dizzying heights of European and international success.

Manchester United is synonymous with success, and this book explores the glory and tragedy that have defined the club's legacy. No conversation about Manchester United would be complete without honouring the incredible players who have graced the pitch in the famous red shirt. The Busby Babes, a group of talented young players whose lives were tragically cut short in the Munich air disaster, will forever be remembered for their immense potential and what might have been. The Holy Trinity of George Best, Bobby Charlton, and Denis Law captivated crowds with their silky skills and flamboyant flair. The class of '92, featuring Ryan Giggs, David Beckham, Paul Scholes, Nicky Butt, and the Neville brothers, rose through the youth ranks to become global household names. And in more recent times, the modern age of global superstars such as Cristiano Ronaldo, Wayne Rooney, Zlatan Ibrahimovic, Marcus Rashford, and Bruno Fernandes. These names, and many more, have continued to grow the club's legacy, by etching their names in the annals of United folklore.

Behind every successful team is a great manager, pacing the touchline, screaming at the players, checking their watch, or chewing gum with intensity. Manchester United has been blessed with some of the most successful and iconic managers in the game. Sir Matt Busby had his team of extraordinary young players torn apart in the Munich air disaster. Had it not been for the heroics of his goalkeeper he would have certainly died in the crash along with so many others. A true survivor, he recovered and rebuilt the club and went on to defy all the odds and lift the European Cup just a decade later. This was an achievement that elevated the club to an almost spiritual level. Sir Alex Ferguson's unmatched dominance of the Premier League era, along with the unforgettable treble-winning campaign, solidified his status as arguably the greatest club manager of all time. His infamous mind games were legendary and his hairdryer treatment was feared by any player that stepped foot in his dressing room. So influential was Ferguson that time itself seems to have been marked by his reign, and even today when fans fondly utter the phrase "Fergie time" it conjures up the memories of magical moments of late comebacks and dramatic victories.

As you embark on this challenging and exciting journey you are invited to consume the book in any way you want. You move chronologically, starting with the club's origins and history, through goalkeeping greats, defensive giants, midfield masters and fantastic forwards.

Then into managers, captains, player personalities, trophies, transfers and starting lineups. Or you pick and choose chapters at random. The book is laid out in a user-friendly way so either option will work. Both allow you to find answers and refer back to them whenever you desire. Whichever tactic you decide to use, the goal is to enjoy acquiring a wealth of knowledge about the mighty Red Devils that will stay with you throughout your long, hopefully successful, but often painful, love affair with the club.

Throughout its history the club has had extraordinary highs and heartbreaking lows, there have been memorable moments of skill, excitement, passion and rivalries. The Red Devils have left an indelible mark on the beautiful game. So please, prepare to immerse yourself in the wonderful world of Manchester United—a club unlike any other.

Good luck!

Glory! Glory! Man United!

Chapter 1
ORIGINS

George Best

THE EARLY YEARS

1. **What year was the club founded?**
   a) 1870   b) 1878   c) 1888   d) 1893

2. **What was the club's original name?**
   a) Newton Heath LYR   b) St Domingo   c) Waterloo SLT
   d) Salford stags

3. **What was the nickname of the club in the late 1800s?**
   a) The Trainmen   b) The red army   c) The Heathens   d) The horns

4. **What colour shirt did the club wear when it was originally formed?**
   a) Red & White   b) Blue & Black   c) Green & Gold   d) Blue & white

5. **On 20th November, 1880, played their first competitive game against the Bolton Wanderer reserve team. They lost by what score?**
   a) 2-0   b) 3-0   c) 5-0   d) 6-0

6. **What was the club's first home ground?**
   a) North Road   b) South Road   c) Bank Street   d) Stretford Street

7. **In what year did the club join the Football League?**
   a) 1892   b) 1896   c) 1899   d) 1900

8. **What position did they finish in their first season?**
   a) 1st   b) 5th   c) 14th   d) 20th

9. **In what year did the club change its name to Manchester United FC?**
   a) 1897   b) 1899   c) 1902   d) 1905

10. **Sir Matt Busby coined the nickname "The Red Devils" in the aftermath of the Munich Air disaster in 1958. Which local rugby club did he take the name from?**
    a) The Salford Red Devils   b) The Old Trafford Red Devils
    c) The Manchester Red Devils   d) The Bury Red Devils

Answers: Page 24

CLUB BADGE ORDER

Can you match the historic Manchester United
badges to the year you think they were used?

a.

b.

c.

d.

e.

f.

g.

1) 1878 – 1902
2) 1902 – 1943
3) 1943 – 1960
4) 1960 – 1970
5) 1970 – 1973
6) 1973 – 1998
7) 1998 – present

Answers: Page 24

OLD TRAFFORD

1. Who origionally came up with the stadium's nickname, "The Theatre of Dreams"?
   a) Sir Matt Busby b) George Best c) Sir Bobby Charlton
   d) Denis Law

2. What year was the first game at Old Trafford played?
   a) 1884 b) 1909 c) 1910 d) 1902

3. Which team did United beat 4−3 in the first match at Old Trafford?
   a) Liverpool b) Manchester City c) Aston Villa d) Chelsea

4. Who has scored the most goals (138) at Old Trafford?
   a) Sir Bobby Charlton b) Denis law c) Wayne Rooney
   d) George Best

5. Manchester United's all-time record attendance at Old Trafford came when they beat Blackburn Rovers 4-1 on 31st March 2007. How many fans were in the ground that day?
   a) 70,162 b) 76,098 c) 84,569 d) 91,260

6. What was the lowest attendance set on 29th April 1950 when Man United beat Fulham 3−0
   a) 9,297 b) 10,624 c) 11,968 d) 12,108

7. Old Trafford hosted the 2003 Champions League final between Juventus and AC Milan. What was the score?
   a) 0-0 b) 1-1 c) 2-2 d) 3-3

8. Between 1941 - 1949 the team couldn't play at Old Trafford because of bomb damage suffered during the war. Which ground did they play at for £5,000 a year rent whilst the stadium was rebuilt?
   a) Anfield b) Main Road c) Boundary Park d) Edgeley Park

9. Which opposition manager played the most games at Old Trafford?
   a) Brian Clough b) Arsene Wenger c) Harry Redknapp
   d) Bill Shankly

10. How many times have England's home international matches been player at Old Trafford?
    a) 6 b) 10 c) 13 d) 17

Answers: Page 24

THE BUSBY BABES

1. The Busby Babes refers to the players who won the league title in 1955-56 and 1956-57. What was their average age?
    a) 19 b) 22 c) 23 d) 24

2. The Manchester Evening News first coined the term "Busby Babes" in which year?
    a) 1951 b) 1955 c) 1956 d) 1958

3. In the last League game the Busby Babes played in front of their adoring supporters at Old Trafford, they beat Bolton Wanderers by what score?
    a) 4-1 b) 5-4 c) 3-0 d) 7-2

4. Which team United beat 5-4 in the last match they played in England before the fateful trip? A match often described as 'one of the greatest games ever seen'?
    a) Arsenal b) Brentford c) Tottenham Hotspur d) Everton

5. What year was the Munich air disaster?
    a) 1957 b) 1958 c) 1959 d) 1960

6. The Munich air disaster occurred on the team's way back home from a European Cup quarter-final victory against which club?
    a) Benfica b) Red Star Belgrade c) Anderlecht d) Bayern Munich

7. How many players died in the Munich air disaster on 6th February 1958?
    a) 6 b) 7 c) 8 d) 9

8. The players became known as "The _____ of Manchester"
    a) Hearts b) Children c) legends d) Flowers

9. Jackie Blanchflower and which other player survived the crash but would never play again?
    a) Johnny Berry b) Harry Gregg c) Kenny Morgans
    d) Albert Scanlon

10. Which player has been described as 'The Last Busby Babe'?
    a) Bobby Charlton b) Sammy McIlroy c) Brian Kidd d) George Best

Answers: Page 24

KIT MANUFACTURERS

Can you match the Manchester United kit manufacturers to the time they were used?

1) 1945 – 1975
2) 1975 – 7980
3) 1980 – 1992
4) 1992 – 2002
5) 2002 – 2015
6) 2015 – present

Answers: Page 24

KIT SPONSORS

Can you match the Manchester United kit
sponsors to the time they were used?

1) 1982 – 2000
2) 2000 – 2006
3) 2006 – 2010
4) 2010 – 2014
5) 2014 – 2021
6) 2021 – present

Answers: Page 24

FUN FACTS, STORIES AND STATS

1. Founded in 1878 as Newton Heath LYR Football Club, Manchester United and was initially a football club for the workers of the Wagon and Carriage Department of the Newton Heath Railroad company, where the players were employed. The team initially played against other departments and railway companies. Then, in 1880, they played their first competitive match against Bolton Wanderers reserves, where they lost 6-0.

2. In 1888, the club became a founding member of a regional league competition called The Combination. A year later, that league was disbanded, so Newton Heath joined the newly formed Football Alliance. Within three years the Football Alliance had merged with the Football League. Then in 1892, the club began competing in the First Division but played as Newton Heath after the LYR was removed from the name.

3. In January 1902, Newton Heath found itself on the verge of bankruptcy. Club captain Harry Stafford convinced four local businessmen to each invest £500 into the club in return for a direct interest in the running of it. As a mark of this fresh start, on 24th April 1902, the club changed its name to "Manchester United" and John Henry Davies became the club's president.

4. Originally the club played in green and gold, the official colours of the Newton Heath railway company. In 1928 this changed to the famous red, black, and white colours, which have been the team colours ever since

5. Between 1878 to 1893 the club played their home games at North Road, which was located close to the railway company. Between 1893 to 1910, they played at Bank Street. Finally, in 1910 they moved to Old Trafford, nicknamed "The Theatre of Dreams". They beat Liverpool 4-3 in their first-ever match and have been playing their home games ever since.

6. The first great era in Manchester United's history was created by the Scotsman, Sir Matt Busby. He built the famous Busby Babes, a group of young and exciting players that won their first league title with an average age of 22. 10 out of the 11 'Busby Babes' were Englishmen, and seven of them had already represented England as full internationals by the time of the Munich disaster.

7. Tragedy struck for the Busby Babes on 6th February 1958, when the plane carrying the squad home from a Europan Cup quarter-final against Red Star Belgrade, went down in Munich shortly after refuelling. Twenty-three lives, including 8 of the players, were lost in the "Munich Air Disaster". The legend of the "flowers of Manchester" lives on

8. On 10th February 2008, to honour the 50th anniversary of those who lost the lives lost in the Munich Air Disaster, the team played Manchester City wearing shirts designed like those worn back in 1958

9. Old Trafford was almost completely destroyed in World War II due to bombing damage. Whilst it was being rebuilt, the team played its home games at Maine Road, the home of rivals Manchester City, for a fee of £5,000 plus a small percentage of gate receipts.

10. Due to the all-seating rules introduced in 1993, the capacity of the stadium was reduced to 44,000. Huge development in the ground has meant that the stadium can now hold a capacity of 75,957.

TRIVIA QUIZ ANSWERS
Chapter 1: Origins

THE EARLY YEARS
1. b) 1878
2. a) Newton Heath LYR
3. c) The Heathens
4. c) Green & Gold
5. d) 6-0
6. a) North Road
7. a) 1892
8. d) 20th
9. c) 1902
10. a) The Salford Red Devils

THE BUSBY BABES
1. b) 22
2. a) 1951
3. d) 7-2
4. a) Arsenal
5. b) 1958
6. b) Red Star Belgrade
7. c) 8
8. d) Flowers
9. a) Johnny Berry
10. d) George Best

CLUB BADGE ORDER
1. b
2. g
3. c
4. a
5. e
6. d
7. f

KIT MANUFACTURERS
1. Umbro
2. Admiral
3. Adidas
4. Umbro
5. Adidas
6. Nike

OLD TRAFFORD
1. c) Sir Bobby Charlton
2. c) 1910
3. a) Liverpool
4. a) Sir Bobby Charlton
5. b) 76,098
6. c) 11,968
7. a) 0-0
8. b) Main Road
9. b) Arsene Wenger
10. d) 17

KIT SPONSORS
1. Sharp
2. Vodaphone
3. AIG
4. AON
5. Chevrolet
6. Team Viewer

Chapter 2
CLUB HISTORY

THE NUMBER 7 SHIRT

1. Since 1968 how many players have worn the number 7 shirt?
   a) 7 b) 9 c) 12 d) 14

2. Which number did David Beckham wear before taking the famous number 7 in the 1997-1998 season?
   a) 8 b) 10 c) 14 d) 23

3. Alex Ferguson wanted which player to be Manchester United's No. 7 before David Beckham took it
   a) Roy Keane b) Paul Scholes c) Nicky Butt d) Jordi Cruyff

4. Which of these players did not regularly wear the number 7 for United?
   a) Bobby Charlton b) Steve Coppell c) Andrei Kanchelskis
   d) Nobby Stiles

5. After Ronaldo left the club in 2009, who took the number 7 shirt?
   a) Nani b) Danny Welbeck c) Anderson d) Michael Owen

6. In the 10 years after Cristiano Ronaldo's departure in 2009, 5 players have worn the number 7 shirt. How many Premier League goals did they score in total?
   a) 15 b) 30 c) 45 d) 70

7. How many players have won the Ballon d'Or whilst wearing the number 7?
   a) 1 b) 2 c) 3 d) 4

8. Which player has worn the number 7 shirt for the longest period of time in Manchester United's history?
   a) George Best b) Bryan Robson c) David Beckham
   d) Cristiano Ronaldo

9. Who wore the number 7 from 1992-1997?
   a) Brian McClair b) Keith Gillespie c) Ryan Giggs d) Eric Cantona

10. Who gave up the number 7 in 2021 to allow Cristiano Ronaldo to take it back?
    a) Bruno Fernandes b) Antonio Valencia c) Edinson Cavani
    d) Marcus Rashford

Answers: Page 35

THE CLASS OF 92

1. David Beckham, Ryan Giggs, Nicky Butt, Paul Scholes, Gary Neville and Phil Neville all went on to have glittering careers for Manchester United after winning which youth competition?
   a) The FA youth Cup b) The Youth League c) The Europa Youth Cup
   d) Lancashire FA Challenge Trophy

2. Which member of the class made his senior debut for the club first?
   a) David Beckham b) Ryan Giggs c) Paul Scholes d) Gary Neville

3. Which coach is credited with developing the group at youth level?
   a) Brian Kidd b) Eric Harrison d) Mike Phelan e) Tommy Burns

4. Who was the only member of the class to be sent out on loan by Manchester United?
   a) Paul Scholes b) Phil Neville c) David Beckham d) Nicky Butt

5. Who is the youngest member of the class of 92
   a) Gary Neville b) Phil Neville c) Nicky Butt d) Paul Scholes

6. Who was the first member to leave the club?
   a) Phil Neville b) Nicky Butt c) Paul Scholes d) David Beckham

7. Who was the last to leave the club?
   a) Paul Scholes b) David Beckham c) Gary Neville d) Ryan Giggs

8. Who was the first to go into management?
   a) Nicky Butt b) Paul Scholes c) Gary Neville d) Ryan Giggs

9. Which club did the class of 92 buy along with Peter Lim in 2014
   a) Salford FC b) Oldham Athletic c) Bury FC
   d) FC United of Manchester

10. Which member of the class was caught calling Robbie Savage a knobhead on live TV?
    a) David Beckham b) Gary Neville c) Paul Scholes d) Nicky Butt

Answers: Page 35

THE MANCHESTER DERBY

1. The first meeting between the two teams was in 1881. United were called Newton Heath, what was Machester City's name at the time?
   a) Hyde Road XI b) West Gorton c) Ardwick AFC d) St Mark's

2. Which player has scored the most goals in the Derby, with 11?
   a) Eric Cantona b) Bobby Charlton c) Wayne Rooney
   d) Mark Hughes

3. How many miles apart are the two teams' stadiums?
   a) 2 b) 4 c) 6 d) 8

4. Manchester City unveiled a billboard of Carlos Tevez in the city centre after signing him from United. What did the billboard read?
   a) Why always me? b) The bigger club
   c) Manchester is blue d) Welcome to Manchester

5. Which of these players did not play for both clubs?
   a) Brian McClair b) Owen Hargreaves c) Peter Schmeichel
   d) Andy Cole

6. There have been three hat tricks scored in Premier League derby matches. Phil Foden and Erling Haaland scored two of them, who scored the other for United?
   a) Andrei Kanchelskis b) Andy Cole c) Dwight Yorke
   d) Michael Owen

7. What is United's longest unbeaten streak against City?
   a) 8 games b) 12 games c) 14 games d) 16 games

8. The two sides have only met once in a major final, but in how many semi-finals of the FA and League Cup combined have they met?
   a) 0 b) 1 c) 4 d) 6

9. Mark Hughes and which former teammates have managed City?
   a) Steve Coppell b) Bryan Robson c) Gordon Strachan
   d) Mark Robins

10. City and United players put aside their differences in 1978 for a Merseyside vs Manchester fixture for whose testimonial?
    a) Denis Law b) Bobby Charlton c) Francis Lee d) Colin Bell

Answers: Page 35

THE NORTHWEST DERBY

1. The rivalry between Manchester and Liverpool dates back to what era?
   a) 1952 b) First World War c) Industrial Revolution
   d) Second World War

2. The first meeting between the two teams in 1894 was played where?
   a) Bolton b) Blackburn c) Accrington d) Stockport

3. Who was once quoted as saying, "I can't stand Liverpool, I can't stand the people, I can't stand anything to do with them."
   a) Sir Alex Ferguson b) Paul Scholes c) Ryan Giggs d) Gary Neville

4. Phil Chisnall was the last player to transfer directly between the two clubs in which year?
   a) 1954 b) 1957 c) 1960 d) 1964

5. How many times have the two teams met in the FA Cup final?
   a) 1 b) 2 c) 3 d) 4

6. United's League Cup win in 2023 tied the number of trophies each club had at how many?
   a) 60 b) 62 c) 67 d) 70

7. As of 2023, how many times have the two teams won the league title combined?
   a) 37 b) 39 c) 42 d) 44

8. Liverpool recorded the biggest win in the fixture in 2023, winning by what score?
   a) 6-0 b) 7-0 c) 7-1 d) 8-0

9. In the 211 meetings between the sides, Liverpool have won 60, how many have United won?
   a) 55 b) 61 c) 68 d) 73

10. As of 2022, how many times has neither side finished in the top two in the Premier League era?
    a) 2 b) 3 c) 4 d) 5

Answers: Page 35

A SEASON TO FORGET

1. In which year was Manchester United relegated from the English first division?
    a) 1972 b) 1973 c) 1974 d) 1975

2. Who was the manager of Manchester United during their relegation season?
    a) Sir Matt Busby b) Tommy Docherty c) Frank O'Farrell
    d) Dave Sexton

3. Whose contract was cancelled midway through the season after just 12 appearances and two goals?
    a) Denis Law b) George Best c) Brian Kidd d) Willie Morgan

4. How many points below safety did Manchester United finish?
    a) 1 b) 2 c) 3 d) 5

5. On the penultimate day of the season United were beaten by Manchester City 1-0. Which former Manchester United legend scored the winning goal?
    a) Bobby Charlton b) Denis Law c) George Best d) George Graham

6. Lou Macari and Sammy McIlroy top scored for United with how many goals each in all competitions?
    a) 6 b) 8 c) 10 d) 12

7. They were knocked out of the League Cup by Second Division winners Middlesbrough, who were managed by which World Cup winner?
    a) Gordon Banks b) George Cohen c) Geoff Hurst d) Jack Charlton

8. United never scored more than three goals in a game that season, how many times did they concede more than three?
    a) 0 b) 8 c) 12 d) 16

9. How long did Manchester United spend in the Second Division?
    a) 1 season b) 2 seasons c) 3 seasons d) 4 seasons

10. Where did they finish on their return to the top flight in 1975-76?
    a) 3rd b) 5th c) 9th d) 15th

Answers: Page 35

FUN FACTS, STORIES AND STATS

1. The significance of the number 7 shirt started with George Best in the 1960's and has been part of the clubs folklore ever since. Bryan Robson once said, "All of a sudden I started playing in the centre of midfield, and I was wearing number 7 all of the time, and I just felt like this was a lucky number for me, and I wore it for the next twelve years." Eric Cantona was the next. He said "In general, I should be a number ten, but at Manchester United, it means something more. Manchester was a city for the number 7. The number 7 is someone who can create things, sometimes one who needs to be free."

2. The class of '92 is a name given to the six young players that rose through the Man United youth system together. David Beckham, Nicky Butt, Ryan Giggs, Gary Neville, Phil Neville and Paul Scholes. They all went on to win numerous trophies with the club including the treble in 1998-99.

3. The 2013 British documentary film called Class of '92 covers the period from Manchester United's FA Youth Cup win in 1992 to the group's Treble-winning 1998/99 season. The film is intercut with the cultural and social changes that took place in Great Britain during that time.

4. Former Welsh international, TV pundit and reality star Robbie Savage started his career at Man United. He couldn't quite make it through the youth team and into the first team and left the club in 1994. He went on to play for Crewe Alexandra, Leicester City, Birmingham City, Blackburn Rovers, Derby County, and Brighton & Hove Albion and played also made 39 appearances for Wales.

5. Michael Owen's first goal at Old Trafford came in stoppage time in the Manchester derby to give United a 4-3 win. Owen has scored in four derbies, the Manchester derby, the Merseyside derby, El Clásico and the Tyne-Wear derby.

6. Having come through the youth ranks David Beckham was always destined for greatness and it felt inevitable that the number 7 would be his eventually. "As a United fan, I was always aware of how important the number 7 shirt was." He had just had one of the best seasons wearing the number ten when he was told that incoming striker Teddy Sheringham would be taking that number. After arriving for pre-season training, Becks was invited into Sir Alex Ferguson's office and was told he was getting the number 7. "I think I cried," he says. "My dad was the first person that I phoned. He was a hardcore United fan, so for his son to be playing for Manchester United and wearing the number 7 shirt! I knew how important that was."

7. Manchester United's joint biggest league defeat came in March 2023 during the North-West derby. Liverpool hammered them 7-0 with goals from Salah, Gakpo, Núñez and Firmino

8. There have only been three hat tricks scored in the Manchester derby. The first one was scored by Andrei Kanchelskis in a 5-0 win at Old Trafford in November 1994. The other two were both scored in the same game. Phil Foden and Erling Haaland scored in Manchester City's 6-3 victory at the Etihad Stadium in October 2022.

9. David Beckham, Gary and Phil Neville, Ryan Giggs, Nicky Butt and Paul Scholes are the majority shareholders at Salford City. The club now plays in League Two following four promotions since the Class of '92 took ownership of the club.

10. On the last day of the 1973-74 season, United could only avoid relegation by winning their home game against Manchester City. The scorer of the winning goal for Manchester City was former United legend Denis Law, who scored in the 81st minute with a back-heel. He did not celebrate the goal. The goal triggered a pitch invasion by the United fans and the referee was forced to abandon the game in the 85th minute. United came straight back up the next season and have been playing in the top division ever since.

TRIVIA QUIZ ANSWERS
Chapter 2: Club History

THE NUMBER 7 SHIRT

1. c) 12
2. b) 10
3. a) Roy Keane
4. a) Bobby Charlton
5. d) Michael Owen
6. a) 15
7. b) 2
8. a) George Best
9. d) Eric Cantona
10. c) Edinson Cavani

THE CLASS OF 92

1. a) The FA youth Cup
2. b) Ryan Giggs
3. b) Eric Harrison
4. c) David Beckham
5. b) Phil Neville
6. d) David Beckham
7. d) Ryan Giggs
8. c) Gary Neville
9. a) Salford FC
10. c) Paul Scholes

THE MANCHESTER DERBY

1. d) St Mark's
2. c) Wayne Rooney
3. b) 4
4. d) Welcome to Manchester
5. a) Brian McClair
6. a) Andrei Kanchelskis
7. c) 14 games
8. d) 6
9. a) Steve Coppell
10. d) Colin Bell

THE NORTH WEST DERBY

1. c) Industrial Revolution
2. b) Blackburn
3. d) Gary Neville
4. d) 1964
5. b) 2
6. c) 67
7. b) 39
8. b) 7-0
9. c) 68
10. d) 5

A SEASON TO FOGET

1. c) 1974
2. b) Tommy Docherty
3. b) George Best
4. d) 5
5. b) Denis Law
6. a) 6
7. d) Jack Charlton
8. a) 0
9. a) 1 season
10. a) 3rd

Chapter 3

GOALKEEPING GREATS

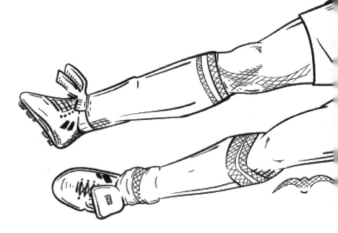

PETER **SCHMEICHEL**

GOALKEEPERS
PART 1

1. On 22nd August 1999 Nick Culkin played his only Premier League game for Man Utd against Arsenal. What was unusual it?
   a) He scored a goal b) It's the shortest debut in the Premier League
   c) He got sent off d) He scored an own goal

2. Who replaced Jim Leighton for the 1990 FA Cup final replay?
   a) Les Sealey b) Mark Bosnich c) Gary Walsh d) Chris Turner

3. Gary Bailey was born in England but grew up and began and ended his career in which country?
   a) New Zealand b) Canada c) Zimbabwe d) South Africa

4. Bailey was United's goalkeeper for how many FA Cup finals?
   a) 1 b) 2 c) 3 d) 4

5. How many appearances did Victor Valdes make for United?
   a) 2 b) 5 c) 8 d) 11

6. In 2023, David de Gea became the second 'keeper to play 400 times for the Red Devils, who was the first?
   a) Harry Gregg b) Alex Stepney c) Peter Schmeichel
   d) Edwin van der Sar

7. Which goalkeeper arrived at Old Trafford having just won the European Championship?
   a) Peter Schmeichel b) David de Gea c) Victor Valdes
   d) Fabien Barthez

8. Who was United's 'keeper for their successful Europa League campaign in 2017?
   a) Dean Henderson b) Sergio Romero c) Lee Grant d) Joel Pereira

9. In which year did Peter Schmeichel win both UEFA Club Goalkeeper of the Year and UEFA Goalkeeper of the Year?
   a) 1992 b) 1996 c) 1998 d) 1999

10. Who is the only goalkeeper to win titles under Sir Alex Ferguson in both England and Scotland?
    a) Andy Goram b) Gary Bailey c) Gary Walsh d) Jim Leighton

Answers: Page 46

GOALKEEPERS
PART 2

1. **Who was the first goalkeeper Sir Alex Ferguson signed for United?**
   a) Jim Leighton b) Les Sealey c) Peter Schmeichel d) Tony Cotton

2. **Who was the only player Fergie signed twice for United?**
   a) Raimond van der Gouw b) Mark Bosnich c) Nick Culkin
   d) Kevin Pilkington

3. **On 1st March 1990 Ipswich Town beat United 6-0. What remarkable thing did their goalkeeper Gary Bailey do?**
   a) He saved 2 penalties b) He saved 3 penalties
   c) He saved 4 penalties d) He played without boots

4. **United made a rare goalkeeping substitution in the 2004 FA Cup final as Tim Howard was replaced by whom?**
   a) Fabien Barthez b) Ricardo c) Roy Carroll d) Paul Rachubka

5. **Harry Gregg received which award in 1958?**
   a) OBE b) Football Writers' Player of the Year
   c) FIFA World Cup Best Goalkeeper d) Ballon d'Or

6. **Whose middle names are Johannes Hendrikus?**
   a) Edwin van der Sar b) Mark Bosnich c) Peter Schmeichel
   d) Raimond van der Gouw

7. **Which goalkeeper returned to Old Trafford in 2021, 11 years after leaving the first time?**
   a) Jack Butland b) Tom Heaton c) Lee Grant d) Martin Dubravka

8. **In the 1967 Comunity Shield, which keeper scored against United?**
   a) Pat Jennings b) Gordon Banks c) Peter Bonetti
   d) Ronnie Hellstrom

9. **Andy Goram and which teammate did not speak to each other during the Scotsman's time on loan?**
   a) Roy Keane b) Gary Neville c) Denis Irwin d) Laurent Blanc

10. **Who spent 13 years playing mainly as a back-up 'keeper, but played in the 1963 FA Cup final in place of the injured Harry Gregg?**
    a) Reg Allen b) David Gaskell c) Jack Crompton d) Ray Wood

Answers: Page 46

ALEX STEPNEY

1. **Manchester United signed Stepney from which club in 1966?**
   a) Arsenal b) Chelsea c) Tottenham Hotspur d) Charlton Athletic

2. **At which club did he begin his career?**
   a) Faversham FC b) Tooting & Mitcham c) Havant & Waterlooville
   d) Leatherhead

3. **How did Eusebio respond to Stepney making a save against him in the 1968 European Cup final?**
   a) He threw his boots into the crowd b) He stood and applauded
   c) He fell to his knees and cried d) He punched him

4. **Stepney had done what just one week before the European Cup final?**
   a) Win his only England cap b) Hand in a transfer request
   c) Receive a ban from UEFA d) Return from a long-term injury

5. **He was an unused member of the England squad for the 1970 World Cup and which other tournament?**
   a) 1966 World Cup b) Euro 68 c) Euro 72 d) Euro 80

6. **Stepney did what against Leicester City and Birmingham City in 1973?**
   a) Get sent off b) Concede seven goals
   c) Get knocked unconscious d) Score a penalty

7. **How did Stepney dislocate his jaw against Birmingham in 1975?**
   a) Colliding with the post b) Having a powerful shot
   c) Being kicked in the face d) Shouting at his defence

8. **How many clean sheets did Stepney keep for Manchester United?**
   a) 125 b) 150 c) 175 d) 200

9. **How many times did he lose a Wembley final?**
   a) 0 b) 1 c) 2 d) 3

10. **Stepney played in the North American Soccer League after leaving United, playing for which team?**
    a) Dallas Hurricane b) Dallas Avalanche c) Dallas Tornado

Answers: Page 46

PETER SCHMEICHEL

1. What year did Schmeichel join Manchester United?
   a) 1989 b) 1990 c) 1991 d) 1992

2. From which club did they sign him?
   a) FC København b) Malmö FF c) Ajax d) Brøndby IF

3. Schmeichel made a total of 310 premier league appearances. How many clean sheets did he keep?
   a) 108 b) 128 c) 139 d) 151

4. How many goals did Schmeichel score for Manchester United?
   a) 0 b) 1 c) 2 d) 5

5. How many times in total did he captain the club?
   a) 40 b) 45 d) 50 d) 65

6. Against which team did he make his final appearance for the club?
   a) Arsenal b) Bayern Munich d) Juventus d) Chelsea

7. What was the first trophy Schmeichel won with United?
   a) Premier League b) League Cup d) European super cup d) FA Cup

8. How many times did he win UEFA Goalkeeper of the year award?
   a) 1 b) 3 d) 5 d) 7

9. He won the 1992 European Championship with Denmark. Which team did they beat 2-0 in the final?
   a) Germany b) Italy c) Spain d) Holland

10. Schmeichel is the most capped Danish player with how many appearances?
    a) 99 b) 110 c) 129 d) 142

Answers: Page 46

EDWIN VAN DER SAR

1. Van der Sar joined Manchester United in 2005, for a reported £2 million from which club?
   a) Fulham b) West Ham United c) Portsmouth d) Wigan Athletic

2. How old was he when they signed him?
   a) 29 b) 32 c) 34 d) 36

3. How many years separated van der Sar's first Champions League win and his second?
   a) 8 b) 10 c) 11 d) 13

4. How many appearances did he van der Sar make for the Netherlands?
   a) 100 b) 110 c) 120 d) 130

5. His last match for the club was the 2011 Champions League final against Barcelona, what record did he break in that match?
   a) Most saves made in a European final
   b) Oldest player to feature in a Champions League final
   c) First United player to play in three European Cup finals
   d) Fewest touches made in a Champions League final

6. Van Der Sar holds the world record for the longest time without conceding a goal in league football. How many minutes did he keep a clean sheet for?
   a) 1,112 b) 1,223 c) 1,311 d) 1,450

7. In which season did he win the Premier League golden glove?
   a) 2010-11 b) 2008-09 c) 2006-07 d) 2003-04

8. In the 2008 Champions League final against Chelsea Van der Sar saved a penalty to win the trophy. Who did he save it against?
   a) Nicholas Anelka b) John Terry c) Frank Lampard
   d) Didier Drogba

9. Van der Sar was the first non-Italian to play in goal for which club?
   a) Lazio b) Milan c) Juventus d) Parma

10. In 2016, van der Sar became the CEO of which club?
    a) PSV Eindhoven b) Twente c) Feyenoord d) Ajax

Answers: Page 46

DAVID DE GEA

1. Which part of Spain was David De Gea born?
   a) Barcelona b) Madrid c) Valencia d) Mallorca

2. At which club did De Gea begin his professional career?
   a) Atlético Madrid b) Real Madrid C) Cadiz d) Sevilla

3. Which game did De Gea play until the age of 13?
   a) Tennis b) Futsal c) Hockey d) Beach football

4. As a youth player he played in which position?
   a) Right back b) Central defender c) Defensive Midfielder
   d) Striker

5. What year did De Gea sign for Manchester United?
   a) 2010 b) 2011 c) 2012 d) 2013

6. How old was he when he signed for the club?
   a) 19 b) 20 c) 21 d) 22

7. During his time in Spain he won UEFA Europa League and which other trophy?
   a) La liga b) The Spanish Cup c) UEFA Super Cup
   d) The Champions League

8. In 2023, David de Gea equalled Peter Schmeichel's record of how many clean sheets for United?
   a) 145 b) 155 c) 160 d) 180

9. Which eye condition does he have that means he has to wear contact lenses during matches?
   a) Short-sighted b) Long-sighted c) Glaucoma d) Cataract

10. Which Manchester City player did De Gea become good friends with after playing together in Spain?
    a) Sergio Agüero b) David Silva c) Kevin De Bruyne d) Jesús Navas

Answers: Page 46

FUN FACTS, STORIES AND STATS

1. Peter Schmeichel is the only Manchester United goalkeeper to have scored from open play. He scored in a 1995 UEFA Cup tie against Rotor Vologrand, with a header from Ryan Giggs's corner. He also became the first goalkeeper to score in the Premier League when he scored for Aston Villa against Everton with a volley at the far post

2. Alex Stepney was the first Manchester United goalkeeper to score for the club. In the 1973-74 season, he scored two penalties. The club were having a terrible season and his two goals meant he was the club's joint-leading goalscorer at Christmas. The club went on to get relegated at the end of the season.

3. Peter Schmeichel is arguably Man Utd's most successful goalkeeper. He made 180 clean sheets in total. In all his seasons playing for Man United, he hit double-figures for clean sheets. His highest was in the 1994/95 season when he had 22 in 33 games. He won 15 major trophies at the club, including 5 Premier League and captained the club when they won the Champions League in 1999. A true United legend

4. After Schmeichel left Manchester United in 1999, the club spent many years trying to replace him. Mark Bosnich, Massimo Taibi, Fabian Barthez, Tim Howard, and Roy Carroll all tried unsuccessfully to fill the gloves of the Great Dane. It wasn't until Edwin van der Sar signed from Fulham in 2005 that Sir Alex Ferguson found the right man to fill the void.

5. At the age of 40 years, 211 days, Edwin Van der Sar was the oldest player to ever play in a Champions League final. Manchester United lost 3-1 to Barcelona in the 2011 final. This was Van der Sar's final match for the club before his retirement. He was also the oldest player ever to win the Premier League at 40 years and 205 days old. Age really is just a number.

6. In the 2008-09 season, Van der Sar kept an incredible 21 clean sheets and set a world league record by not conceding a goal for 1,311 minutes.

7. Nick Culkin holds the record for the shortest-ever Premier League debut. He was brought on in stoppage time against Arsenal at Highbury in 1999 when Raimond van der Gouw was injured. Culkin took a free kick and the final whistle blew. Nick Culkin is also the first player to play for Manchester United and non-league side FC United of Manchester.

8. Northern Ireland international Harry Gregg is one of the great United goalkeepers, however, during his 247 appearances for the club he only won a solitary FA Cup runners-up medal after injuries blighted his career. He was known as 'The Hero of Munich' after he famously survived the crash and then went back into the burning wreckage to rescue a 20-month-old baby and several of his teammates, as well as his manager Sir Matt Busby.

9. Alex Stepney has the most appearances as a goalkeeper in United history, having played 539 times for the club. He helped the club beat Benfica 4-1 in the 1968 European Cup final. Famously making an outstanding close-range save against Portuguese legend Eusébio late in the game, which resulted in him standing and applauding the Englishman.

10. The flamboyant French international Fabien Barthez was prone to making the odd howler, yet he was one of the most entertaining and best keepers to ever play for the club. He joined Man United from Monaco in 2000 after winning the 1998 World Cup on home soil. He shares the World Cup record with England's Peter Shilton for most clean sheets in the tournament with 10.

TRIVIA QUIZ ANSWERS
Chapter 3: Goalkeeping Greats

GOALKEEPERS - PART 1
1. b) It's the shortest debut in the Premier League
2. a) Les Sealey
3. d) South Africa
4. c) 3
5. a) 2
6. b) Alex Stepney
7. d) Fabien Barthez
8. b) Sergio Romero
9. c) 1998
10. d) Jim Leighton

GOALKEEPERS - PART 2
1. a) Jim Leighton
2. b) Mark Bosnich
3. b) He saved 3 penalties
4. c) Roy Carroll
5. c) World Cup Best Goalkeeper
6. d) Raimond van der Gouw
7. b) Tom Heaton
8. a) Pat Jennings
9. a) Roy Keane
10. b) David Gaskell

ALEX STEPNEY
1. b) Chelsea
2. b) Tooting & Mitcham
3. b) He stood and applauded
4. a) Win his only England cap
5. b) Euro 68
6. d) Score a penalty
7. d) Shouting at his defence
8. c) 175
9. b) 1
10. c) Dallas Tornado

PETER SCHMEICHEL
1. c) 1991
2. d) Brøndby IF
3. b) 128
4. b) 1
5. a) 40
6. b) Bayern Munich
7. d) European super cup
8. b) 3
9. a) Germany
10. c) 129

EDWIN VAN DER SAR
1. a) Fulham
2. c) 34
3. d) 13
4. d) 130
5. b) Oldest player to feature in a Champions League final
6. c) 1,311
7. b) 2008–09
8. a) Nicholas Anelka
9. c) Juventus
10. d) Ajax

DAVID DE GEA
1. b) Madrid
2. a) Atlético Madrid
3. b) Futsal
4. d) Striker
5. b) 2011
6. b) 20
7. c) UEFA Super Cup
8. d) 180
9. b) Long sighted
10. a) Sergio Agüero

Chapter 4
DEFENSIVE GIANTS
PART 1

RIO FERDINAND

DEFENDERS
PART 1

1. Who kept a clean sheet against Tottenham Hotspur in 2007 after Edwin van der Sar was taken off injured and there were no more substitutes left?
   a) Rio Ferdinand b) Wes Brown c) Mikael Silvestre d) John O'Shea

2. Harry MaGuire was signed from which club in 2019?
   a) Bolton Wanderers b) Sheffield United c) Leicester City d) Everton

3. Ronny Johnsen played for United and which two other clubs?
   a) Southampton & Tottenham Hotspur
   b) Sheffield Wednesday & Birmingham City
   c) Aston Villa & Newcastle United
   d) Arsenal & Ipswich Town

4. Which defender has made the most appearancees for United?
   a) Gary Neville b) Steve Bruce c) Rio Ferdinand d) Denis Irwin

5. In 1985, which centre back became the first player to be sent off in an FA Cup final?
   a) Gordon McQueen b) Paul McGrath c) Kevin Moran
   d) Mike Duxbury

6. Chris Smalling began his career at which other MUFC?
   a) Marske United b) Maidenhead United c) Maidstone United
   d) Mangotsfield United

7. "The Butcher of Amsterdam" is whose nickname?
   a) Tyrell Malacia b) Lisandro Martinez c) Jaap Stam d) Phil Neville

8. Who played against United in the 1990 FA Cup semi-final, shortly before signing for the Red Devils?
   a) Gary Pallister b) Steve Bruce c) Paul Parker d) Denis Irwin

9. In 2004, which United defender became the first winner of an Olympic gold medal since Harold Hardman in 1908?
   a) Gabriel Heinze b) Gerard Pique c) Patrice Evra d) John O'Shea

10. John O'Shea famously nutmegged who in thw Champions League?
    a) Roberto Carlos b) Ronaldo c) Zinedine Zidane d) Luis Figo

Answers: Page 57

RIO FERDINAND

1. **In Which part of South London was Rio Ferdinand born?**
   a) Clapham   b) Camberwell   c) Croydon   d) Brixton

2. **Which club did he begin his professional career with?**
   a) West Ham   b) Queens Park Rangers   c) Brentford   d) Millwall

3. **Which club was Ferdinand signed from in 2002**
   a) West Ham United   b) Millwall   c) Leeds United   d) QPR

4. **At the time of signing it was a British record transfer fee of how much?**
   a) £15 million   b) £20 million   c) £30 million   d) £40 million

5. **In 2003 Ferdinand was banned for 8 months for doing what?**
   a) Assaulting a referee   b) Making an offensive gesture
   c) Failing to pay a fine   d) Missing a drugs test

6. **In 2006 Ferdinand produced and presented his own TV show called what?**
   a) Rio's world cup wind up   b) You've been merked
   c) Rio's Rio adventure   d) South of the river

7. **Ferdinand scored 8 goals for United, who was the only team he scored more than once against?**
   a) Newcastle United   b) West Ham United   c) Chelsea   d) Liverpool

8. **How many caps did Ferdinand win in his 14-year England career?**
   a) 81   b) 91   c) 101   d) 111

9. **In the 12 years that Ferdinand played for the club, how many Premier League titles did he win**
   a) 6   b) 7   c) 8   d) 10

10. **Which club did Ferdinand play 12 games for after leaving United?**
    a) Queens Park Rangers   b) Charlton Athletic   c) Fulham   d) Luton

Answers: Page 57

NEMAJA VIDIC

1. **Which club was Vidic signed from in January 2006?**
   a) Spartak Moscow b) Red star Belgrade c) Dinamo Kiev
   d) Hajduk Split

2. **When United signed him, which player left the club during the same transfer window?**
   a) Diego Forlan b) Kleberson c) Quinton Fortune d) David Bellion

3. **Vidic was part of the 'Famous Four' Serbian defence of the 2006 World Cup Qualification Campaign, but how many goals did they concede?**
   a) 0 b) 1 c) 3 d) 5

4. **How many appearances did he make for Serbia?**
   a) 28 b) 43 c) 56 d) 67

5. **During his time at the club, how many times did he win the Premier League Player of the Season?**
   a) 1 b) 2 c) 3 d) 4

6. **Sir Alex once said about Vidic "How many centre-halves can you name who actually like _____"**
   a) Attacking b) Scoring c) Defending d) Partying

7. **How many times was Vidic a Premier League title winner?**
   a) 4 b) 5 c) 6 d) 7

8. **He made exactly how many appearances in a United shirt?**
   a) 150 b) 200 c) 250 d) 300

9. **Vidic received a total of 4 red cards against one club, more than any other player against an opponent in Premier League history. Which club was it?**
   a) Manchester City b) Chelsea c) Liverpool d) Arsenal

10. **After leaving in 2014 Viidic made 28 appearances for which club?**
    a) AC Milan b) Fiorentina c) Inter Milan d) Juventus

Answers: Page 57

STEVE BRUCE

1. For which Kent club did Bruce begin his professional career?
   a) Southend b) Gillingham FC c) Dover Athletic
   d) Faversham Town

2. In which year did Bruce sign for Manchester United?
   a) 1985 b) 1987 c) 1988 d) 1989

3. Which club did Manchester United sign Bruce from for £825,000?
   a) Oldham Athletic b) Southampton c) Norwich City d) Brentford

4. Bruce was United's captain for much of the 1992/93 premier league season due to which player missing games through injury?
   a) Bryan Robson b) Dennis Irwin c) Paul Ince d) Mark Hughes

5. Despite a glittering club career how many England caps did Bruce receive?
   a) 0 b) 2 c) 5 d) 7

6. During the 1990/91 season Bruce was the club's joint top scorer with Byran McClair with 19 goals. How many of those were penalties?
   a) 7 b) 9 c) 11 d) 13

7. How many trophies did Bruce win whilst at Manchester United?
   a) 6 b) 8 c) 9 d) 11

8. Which club did Bruce join when he left United in 1996?
   a) Birmingham City b) Norwich City c) Bristol City
   d) Wigan Athletic

9. Which one of these clubs has Bruce NOT managed
   a) Crystal Palace b) Sunderland c) Hull City d) Preston North End

10. What is the title of Bruce's autobiography?
    a) Full Back b) No Guts, No Glory c) Head Strong
    d) Heading for Victory

Answers: Page 57

GARY PALLISTER

1. **Either side of the nine years playing for Manchester United, Pallister played for which club?**
   a) Sunderland b) Middlesbrough c) Oldham Athletic d) Fulham

2. **The fee Manchester United paid for Pallister in 1989 was the record transfer between two British clubs at the time. What was the fee?**
   a) £1.8 million b) £2 million c) £2.3 million d) £2.75 million

3. **He won which award in the 1991/92 season?**
   a) Match of the Day Goal of the Season b) PFA Player of the Year
   c) Sir Matt Busby Player of the Year d) Ballon d'Or

4. **"Dolly & Daisy" was Sir Alex Ferguson's nickname for Pallister and which teammate?**
   a) Steve Bruce b) David May c) Phil Neville d) Denis Irwin

5. **What was unusual about Pallister's England debut?**
   a) He scored b) It was a World Cup c) He didn't touch the ball
   d) He was a Second Division player at the time

6. **Pallister scored his only goal of the 1992-93 title-winning season in Man United's final home match of the season by which method?**
   a) Direct free kick b) Penalty kick c) Header d) Bicycle kick

7. **He scored twice against which team to win the title in 1996-97?**
   a) Arsenal b) Newcastle United c) Liverpool d) Leeds United

8. **His only goal in Europe was scored against which club?**
   a) FC Porto b) Red Star Belgrade c) Juventus d) Wrexham

9. **Not including Charity Shields, how many trophies did Pallister win in his nine years at Old Trafford?**
   a) 7 b) 8 c) 9 d) 10

10. **Which former United teammate was his next manager after leaving Old Trafford in 1998?**
    a) Clayton Blackmore b) Bryan Robson c) Lee Martin
    d) Mark Hughes

Answers: Page 57

FUN FACTS, STORIES AND STATS

1. Rio Ferdinand and Nemanja Vidic are one of the most successful partnerships in Premier League history. They started 187 games together and kept an incredible 91 clean sheets.

2. The Serbian international Nemanja Vidic joined United from Spartak Moscow in January 2006. He was named the Premier League Player of the Season twice, and he was included in the PFA Team of the Year four times. He was a ruthless defender and helped the club win five Premier League titles, three League Cups, one FIFA Club World Cup, and the Champions League, before joining Inter Milan in 2014.

3. Rio Ferdinand played 504 times in the Premier League, 312 of those matches was for Man United. Ferdinand was an England regular for most of his career and made 81 senior appearances, scoring three goals. Rio is the brother of Anton and cousin of Kane and Les Ferdinand. All of whom have played professionally.

4. French international Patrice Evra also joined Man United in January 2006 from Monaco. The 5-foot-8-inch defender was renowned for his speed, agility and crossing ability. He won five English Premier League titles and a Champions League before joining Juventus

5. Spanish international Gerard Pique will be remembered as one of the greatest defenders in history after his unparalleled success with Barcelona. It's easy to forget that he began his professional career at Old Trafford. The centre-back only made 23 appearances in his 4 years at the club before arriving back at Barcelona in 2008, the club where he spent his youth. Whilst with the Catalan giants he won every trophy on offer.

6. Steve Bruce and Gary Pallister formed one of the toughest defensive pairings of the 1990s. With these two at the heart of their defence, United won the Premier League, the FA Cup, the League Cup, the European Cup-Winner's Cup and the Super Cup.

7. Steve Bruce is the defender with the most number of goals for Manchester United. Bruce played 414 times for the club and scored 51 goals. Many with his head. After hanging up his boots, Bruce has gone on to have a successful managerial career, taking charge of Birmingham City, Aston Villa and Newcastle to name a few.

8. The current club captain, Harry Maguire, is the most expensive defender in football history. Manchester United reportedly paid Leicester City £85 million in 2019. He is England's highest-ever scoring defender with 7 goals.

9. John O'Shea may not be as famous as his throughout the 2000s, but here is a dependable figure who still played nearly 400 games for the club. Capable of playing anywhere in defence or even in central midfield, O'Shea was a five-time Premier League winner, as well having FA Cup, League Cup and Champions League medals.

10. Tony Dunne was in the starting line up for most of the 1960s. He helped the club win the FA Cup, two league titles and the European Cup. He made 535 appearances which is a record for an Irishman at the club.

TRIVIA QUIZ ANSWERS
Chapter 4: Defensive Giants - Part 1

DEFENDERS - PART 1

1. d) John O'Shea
2. c) Leicester City
3. c) Aston Villa & Newcastle United
4. a) Gary Neville
5. c) Kevin Moran
6. c) Maidstone United
7. b) Lisandro Martinez
8. d) Denis Irwin
9. a) Gabriel Heinze
10. d) Luis Figo

RIO FERDINAND

1. b) Camberwell
2. a) West Ham
3. c) Leeds United
4. c) £30 million
5. d) Missing a drugs test
6. a) Rio's world cup wind up
7. d) Liverpool
8. a) 81
9. a) 6
10. a) Queens Park Rangers

NEMANJA VIDIC

1. a) Spartak Moscow
2. d) David Bellion
3. b) 1
4. c) 56
5. b) 2
6. c) Defending
7. b) 5
8. d) 300
9. c) Liverpool
10. c) Inter Milan

GARY PALLISTER

1. b) Middlesbrough
2. c) £2.3 million
3. b) PFA Player of the Year
4. a) Steve Bruce
5. d) He was a Second Division player at the time
6. a) Direct free kick
7. c) Liverpool
8. d) Wrexham
9. d) 10
10. b) Bryan Robson

STEVE BRUCE

1. b) Gillingham FC
2. b) 1987
3. c) Norwich City
4. a) Bryan Robson
5. a) 0
6. c) 11
7. c) 9
8. a) Birmingham City
9. d) Preston North End
10. d) Heading for Victory

Chapter 5
DEFENSIVE GIANTS
PART 2

GARY
NEVILLE

DEFENDERS
PART 2

1. In 2019 United broke the world transfer record by signing who?
   a) Raphael Varane b) Victor Lindelof c) Aaron Wan-Bissaka
   d) Harry Maguire

2. United's two defenders in the 1968 European Cup final were from which country?
   a) Wales b) Scotland c) Northern Ireland d) Republic of Ireland

3. Gordon McQueen spent seven years at Manchester United but won his only league title at which club?
   a) Derby County b) Nottingham Forest c) Leeds United d) Everton

4. David May was a United player from 1994 - 2003, but how many times did he play enough games to earn a Premier League winner's medal?
   a) 1 b) 2 c) 3 d) 4

5. Lisandro Martinez came through the youth system at the same Argentinian club as Lionel Messi. Which club?
   a) River Plate b) San Lorenzo c) Boca Juniors d) Newell's Old Boys

6. Which player was signed from Sporting CP in 2014 and went on to make over 100 appearances for the Red Devils?
   a) Matteo Darmian   b) Marcos Rojo   c) Daley Blind   d) Antonio Valencia

7. Laurent Blanc's only Premier League goal was scored away at which club?
   a) Chelsea b) Newcastle United c) Fulham d) Tottenham Hotspur

8. Manchester United signed Paul Parker in which year?
   a) 1987 b) 1988 c) 1990 d) 1991

9. Eric Bailly is from which country?
   a) Ivory Coast b) Cameroon c) Ghana d) Mali

10. How many appearances combined did Gary and Phil Neville make for Manchester United?
    a) 788 b) 888 c) 988 d) 1088

Answers: Page 67

JAAP STAM

1. Jaap Stam began his career with which club?
   a) Willem II b) Vitesse Arnhem c) Go Ahead Eagles d) PEC Zwolle

2. From which club did he join Manchester United in 1998?
   a) Ajax b) Milan c) PSV Eindhoven d) Marseille

3. Who partnered Stam at centre back in the 1999 Champions League final?
   a) Wes Brown b) Henning Berg c) Ronny Johnsen d) David May

4. He scored his only Manchester United goal in a 6-2 win over which opponent?
   a) Leicester City b) Nottingham Forest c) Derby County
   d) Coventry City

5. During his three full seasons in the Premier League, how many times was Stam named in the PFA Team of the Year?
   a) 0 b) 1 c) 2 d) 3

6. Sir Alex Ferguson went on to regret selling Stam for £16 million in 2001 to which Italien side?
   a) Lazio b) Roma c) AC Milan d) Parma

7. At which stage in the three major tournaments he played in, were the Netherlands kocked out?
   a) Group stage b) Quarter-finals c) Semi-finals d) Final

8. What is the name of Stam's autobiography?
   a) Stam on Stam b) Head to Head c) Wall to Wall d) Stam the man

9. He returned to Old Trafford as manager of which team for an FA Cup tie?
   a) Sunderland b) Milton Keynes Dons c) Bristol Rovers d) Reading

10. Which MLS club did Stam manage from 2020 to 2021?
    a) Atlanta United b) Seattle Sounders c) Orlando City
    d) FC Cincinnati

Answers: Page 67

GARY NEVILLE

1. How many clubs did Neville play for during his professional career?
   a) One b) Two c) Three d) Four

2. How many trophies did Neville win at Manchester United?
   a) 14 b) 17 c) 20 d) 22

3. Who said "Gary Neville is the best English right back of his generation"?
   a) David Beckham b) Phil Neville c) Jamie Carragher
   d) Alex Ferguson

4. What is Gary Neville's dad called?
   a) Bill b) Neville c) Barry d) Alex

5. Who is the older brother? Gary or Phil?
   a) Gary b) Phil

6. The Nevilles have a sister called Tracey who played which professional sport for England?
   a) Hockey b) Netball c) Football d) Badminton

7. Which manager gave Neville his first England cap?
   a) Graham Taylor b) Glenn Hoddle c) Kevin Keegan
   d) Terry Venables

8. What is the name of the restaurant that Neville owns with his close friend Ryan Giggs?
   a) Cafe Football b) The trophy cabinet c) Trebles d) Nevilles

9. In the 602 appearances Gary made for United, how many goals did he score?
   a) 2 b) 7 c) 10 d) 15

10. In 2015 Neville became manager of which club?
    a) Villareal b) Fiorentina c) Real Betis d) Parma

Answers: Page 67

DENIS IRWIN

1. **Which city was Denis born in?**
   a) Dublin   b) Derry   c) Cork   Belfast

2. **Which club did Irwin begin his professional career at?**
   a) Everton   b) Notts County   c) Nottingham Forest   d) Leeds United

3. **What year did Irwin sign for Manchester United?**
   a) 1989   b) 1990   c) 1991   d) 1992

4. **Which club did Manchester United sign Irwin from?**
   a) Liverpool   b) Oldham Athletic   c) Wrexham   d) Crystal Palace

5. **How much was Irwin signed for?**
   a) £100,000   b) £400,000   c) £625,000   d) £950,000

6. **Irwin played 529 times for the club, scoring how many goals?**
   a) 11   b) 22   c) 33   d) 44

7. **How many medals did Irwin win during his time at United?**
   a) 7   b) 11   c) 14   d) 17

8. **Which world cup did Irwin represent The Republic of Ireland at?**
   a) 1990   b) 1994   c) 1998   d) 2002

9. **What nickname did Alex Ferguson give him due to his consistency?**
   a) Mr Reliable   b) Safe feet Irwin   c) Eight out of ten Denis
   d) The constant baller

10. **Which team did he join when he left United in 2002?**
    a) Swindon Town   b) Bolton Wanderers   c) Oldham Athletic
    d) Wolverhampton Wanderers

Answers: Page 67

BILL FOULKES

1. Bill Foulkes was born in which town, often associated with rugby league?
   a) Warrington b) Wakefield c) Castleford d) St Helen's

2. Foulkes didn't give up his job working in a coal mine until when?
   a) He made his United debut b) He won the First Division in 1956
   c) He survived the Munich air disaster d) He played for England

3. For how many seasons did Foulkes play for Manchester United?
   a) 16 b) 17 c) 18 d) 19

4. How many goals did the defender score in all those seasons?
   a) 9 b) 14 c) 19 d) 24

5. His only England cap came in 1954 against whom?
   a) Northern Ireland b) Hungary c) Wales d) Belgium

6. Foulkes was given the captaincy after the Munich Air Disaster and held it for how many years?
   a) 1 b) 2 c) 3 d) 4

7. The 1966-67 title was the last of how many he won at Old Trafford?
   a) 2 b) 3 c) 4 d) 5

8. After retirement in 1970, he took which role at United for the next five years?
   a) Assistant manager b) Kitman c) Chief Scout
   d) Youth team coach

9. In which country did Foulkes take the first of his nine managerial jobs?
   a) Japan b) Norway c) South Africa d) United States

10. His European Cup winner's medal was auctioned at Sotheby's in London in 2012, for how much?
    a) £15,000 b) £40,000 c) £68,000 d) £77,000

Answers: Page 67

FUN FACTS, STORIES AND STATS

1. Gary Neville spent his entire 20-year career at Old Trafford. He is the most decorated Manchester United defender of all time, winning 31 trophies. Including twelve Premier Leagues, four FA Cups and two Champions League.

2. Phil Neville always seems to be overshadowed by his older brother Gary, but Phil Neville made 386 appearances for Man United before joining Everton. He also has 59 international caps for England. Both Neville brothers have dabbled in management and both worked as commentators for Sky Sports.

3. Allenby Chilton was among an entire generation of football players across Europe who lost a large portion of their career due to the Second World War. He joined Man United from Liverpool in 1938 and has missed 6 seasons he eventually won the FA Cup in 1948 and League Championship in 1951/52. Chilton was the club's captain immediately prior to the Busby Babes era.

4. Sir Alex Ferguson once said that defender Denis Irwin was his best-ever signing. The free-kick specialist made 529 appearances for United between 1990 and 2002, scoring 33 goals. He played 56 times for the Republic of Ireland. He and former teammate Roy Keane, are the most successful Irish players in history. They each won 19 trophies in their careers. Both used to room with other for away matches.

5. Bill Foulkes is the defender with the most appearances for Manchester United. He played 688 times for the club. After the Munich air disaster, he replaced Roger Bryne as the club captain. He started every single United game in the 1957–58, 1959–60 and 1964–65 seasons. He made one appearance for England, in 1955.

6. In 1985 Kevin Moran became the first player ever to be sent off in an FA Cup final. Despite the red card, United went on to beat Everton 1-0 to lift the trophy.

7. The Dutch giant, Jap Stam joined United in 1998 and won the Premier League in all of his three seasons at the club. However, he was sold to Lazio in 2001 after reports suggested that he had upset Sir Alex Ferguson with certain claims he made in his autobiography Head to Head. Sir Alex Ferguson later admitted that selling him was one of the biggest mistakes of his career.

8. After becoming Manchester United's captain at the tender age of 24, Roger Byrne had his life tragically cut short in the Munich Air Disaster at the age of 28. Before his untimely death in 1958, he was being set up to become the next captain of England after Billy Wright. He won three League titles, two as captain and would have no doubt won plenty more.

9. The Brazilian right-back, Rafael Da Silva joined Manchester United's youth academy in 2005, along with his twin brother Fabio. He made his first-team debut in 2008. During his seven-year spell with Manchester United, Rafael made 170 appearances and won three Premier League titles, one League Cup, and one FIFA Club World Cup. Despite struggling with injuries and inconsistency, Rafael remains a cult hero amongst fans for his passionate displays and memorable goals.

10. Mikael Silvestre was an integral part of United's Premier League domination in the early 2000s. He was a regular starter as either a left-back or centre-back and won four Premier League titles, the FA Cup, League Cup and the Champions League.

TRIVIA QUIZ ANSWERS

Chapter 5: Defensive Giants - Part 2

DEFENDERS - PART 2

1. d) Harry Maguire
2. d) Republic of Ireland
3. c) Leeds United
4. b) 2
5. d) Newell's Old Boys
6. b) Marcos Rojo
7. d) Tottenham Hotspur
8. d) 1991
9. a) Ivory Coast
10. c) 988

JAAP STAM

1. d) PEC Zwolle
2. c) PSV Eindhoven
3. c) Ronny Johnsen
4. a) Leicester City
5. d) 3
6. a) Lazio
7. c) Semi-finals
8. b) Head to Head
9. d) Reading
10. d) FC Cincinnati

GARY NEVILLE

1. a) One
2. c) 20
3. d) Alex Ferguson
4. b) Neville
5. a) Gary
6. b) Netball
7. d) Terry Venables
8. a) Cafe Football
9. b) 7
10. a) Villareal

DENIS IRWIN

1. c) Cork
2. d) Leeds United
3. b) 1990
4. b) Oldham Athletic
5. c) £625,000
6. c) 33
7. b) 11
8. b) 1994
9. c) Eight out of ten Denis
10. d) Wolverhampton Wanderers

BILL FOULKES

1. d) St Helen's
2. d) He played for England
3. c) 18
4. a) 9
5. a) Northern Ireland
6. a) 1
7. c) 4
8. d) Youth team coach
9. d) United States
10. b) £40,000

David
BECKHAM

Chapter 6
MIDFIELD MASTERS
PART 1

MIDFIELDERS
PART 1

1. Karel Poborsky signed after impressing at Euro 96, where he scored a memorable lob against which country?
   a) Portugal b) Denmark c) Germany d) Croatia

2. Bruno Fernandes signed from which club in 2020?
   a) Spoting Lisbon b) Porto c) Athletico Madrid d) Lazio

3. Which 2001 Premier League winner would go on to win the 2014 Conference Play-offs with his hometown club, Cambridge United?
   a) Luke Chadwick b) Jonathan Greening c) Michael Clegg
   d)Michael Stewart

4. David Beckham, Diego Forlan and which other United player scored at the 2002 World Cup?
   a) Paul Scholes b) Quinton Fortune c) Roy Keane
   d) Juan Sebastian Veron

5. Nicky Butt made his Premier League debut in which year?
   a) 1992 b) 1993 c) 1994 d) 1995

6. Nemanja Matic has played under Jose Mourinho at United, Chelsea and which other club?
   a) Inter Milan b) Porto c) Tottenham Hotspur d) Roma

7. After struggling at United, Eric Djemba-Djemba joined which club?
   a) Burnley b) Aston Villa c) West Ham United d) Scunthorpe United

8. Neil Webb and Mike Phelan signed for United in which year?
   a) 1985 b) 1987 c) 1989 d) 1991

9. Used as a midfielder or striker, who scored the winner in the 1985 FA Cup final from central midfield?
   a) Gordon Strachan b) Bryan Robson c) Frank Stapleton
   d) Norman Whiteside

10. Jesper Olsen played in the 1985 final. Which country was he from?
    a) Netherlands b) Norway c) Denmark d) Sweden

Answers: Page 77

DAVID BECKHAM

1. On 17th August 1996 Beckham shot to fame by scoring a wonder goal from inside his own half against which club?
   a) Everton b) Wimbledon c) Middlesbrough d) Southampton

2. Beckham scored his first United goal against which team?
   a) Tottenham hotspur b) Galatasaray c) Crystal Palace d) AC Milan

3. During the world cup knockout defeat to Argentina in 1998, Beckham was sent off for kicking which player?
   a) Gabriel Batistuta b) Juan Sebastián Verón c) Diego Simeone
   d) Claudio lopez

4. In 2001 Beckham scored a last-minute free kick at Old Trafford to send England into the 2002 World Cup. Which team was it against?
   a) Poland b) Greece c) Bulgaria d) Moldova

5. Beckham was only sent off once for United in which competition?
   a) Premier League b) FA Cup c) Champions League
   d) FIFA World Club Cup

6. After an FA cup defeat to Arsenal in 2003, Beckham required stitches for a cut above his eye after Alex Ferguson did what to him?
   a) Threw a bottle at him b) Kicked him in the head
   c) Kicked a boot at him d) Kicked a football at him

7. Beckham was cpatain for how many of his 115 appearances for England?
   a) 90 b) 75 c) 59 d) 38

8. Beckham finished runner-up in the Ballon d'Or in 1999. Which Brazilian international won it that year?
   a) Ronaldo b) Rivaldo c) Ronaldinho d) Roberto Carlos

9. Beckham had made 265 Premier league appearances for United and scored 61 goals. How many direct free kicks did he score?
   a) 11 b) 13 c) 18 d) 23

10. At which club did Beckham finish his career?
    a) LA Galaxy b) AC Milan c) PSG d) Arsenal

Answers: Page 77

PAUL INCE

1. **What is Ince's nickname?**
   a) Lord o' the Manor b) The Boss c) The Guvnor d) The Don

2. **With which club did he begin his career?**
   a) Wimbledon b) Charlton Athletic c) Millwall d) West Ham United

3. **Which of these trophies did Ince win as a Manchester United player?**
   a) UEFA Cup b) Intercontinental Cup
   c) European Cup Winners' Cup d) Champions League

4. **In which season did he win the Sir Matt Busby Player of the Year award?**
   a) 1990-91 b) 1991-92 c) 1992-93 d) 1993-94

5. **Ince left Manchester United in 1995 to join which Italian club?**
   a) Inter Milan b) Sampdoria c) Fiorentina d) Juventus

6. **How many trophies did Ince win at arch-rivals, Liverpool?**
   a) 0 b) 1 c) 2 d) 3

7. **In 1993, Ince became the first black man to do what?**
   a) Score for England b) Captain England
   c) Captain Manchester United d) Win PFA Player of the Year

8. **Ince scored twice in 52 caps for England. What was peculiar about those goals?**
   a) They were scored in the same game
   b) They were both at major tournaments
   c) They were both scored when England had caretaker managers
   d) They were both scored in Italy

9. **Ince had a pre-match ritual. Before every game, he did what?**
   a) Put his left boot on first b) Hug every player in the team
   c) Eat Coco Pops cereal d) Puts his shirt on as he enters the pitch

10. **At which club, located not far from Manchester, did Ince start his managerial career?**
    a) Stockport County b) Bury c) Oldham Athletic
    d) Macclesfield Town

Answers: Page 77

LEE SHARPE

1. **Sharpe was signed by Manchester United from which club?**
   a) Gillingham b) Torquay United c) Shrewsbury Town
   d) Morecambe

2. **He received which award in 1991?**
   a) PFA Young Player of the Year b) Sir Matt Busby Player of the Year
   c) Football Writers' Player of the Year d) Golden Boy

3. **How many England caps did Sharpe win?**
   a) 1 b) 3 c) 6 d) 8

4. **During his time at Manchester United, Sharpe's mother used to organise, what?**
   a) His contracts b) His shopping c) His fitness regime
   d) His fan club

5. **In his final appearance in the Champions League, he scored a backheel against which opponent?**
   a) Real Madrid b) Juventus c) Milan d) Barcelona

6. **In 2003, he had a short spell at Grindavik, a club in which country?**
   a) Iceland b) Norway c) Denmark d) Sweden

7. **Other than Manchester United and Leeds United, which other team did Sharpe play for in the Premier League?**
   a) Portsmouth b) Bradford City c) Middlesbrough
   d) Coventry City

8. **Since retirement, Sharpe has made many television appearances, including a minor role in which soap opera?**
   a) Coronation Street b) Emmerdale c) Hollyoaks d) Eastenders

9. **In 2021, he began entering professional tournaments in which sport?**
   a) Snooker b) Darts c) Fencing d) Golf

10. **What is the name of his autobiography?**
    a) Sharpe Shooter b) Sharpe Wit c) The Real Spice Boy
    d) My Idea of Fun

Answers: Page 77

ROY KEANE

1. **Which part of Ireland was Keane born?**
   a) Dublin b) Cork c) Galway d) Limerick

2. **What year did Keane join Manchester United?**
   a) 1991 b) 1992 c) 1993 d) 1994

3. **Which club did Ununted sign him from?**
   a) Sheffield United b) Everton c) Burnley d) Nottingham Forest

4. **How many red cards did Keane receive during his time at the club?**
   a) 7 b) 11 c) 15 d) 18

5. **Which player did Keane replace when he was made captain in 1997?**
   a) Steve Bruce b) Gary Neville c) Eric Cantona d) Ray Wilkins

6. **Keane missed the 1999 champions league final against Bayern Munich after picking up a yellow card against which team in the semi-final?**
   a) AC Milan b) Juventus c) Real Madrid d) Barcelona

7. **Which player was Keane describing when he said "if it had come to a fight, he could probably have killed me"**
   a) Vinnie Jones b) Patrick Viera c) Alf-Inge Haaland d) Gary Neville

8. **After 12 years at United, Keane left to join which club?**
   a) Rangers b) Celtic c) Sunderland d) Shamrock Rovers

9. **What was the first club Keane became manager of?**
   a) Southampton b) Derby c) Ipswich d) Sunderland

10. **Keane was the Republic of Ireland assistant manager between 2013 and 2018. Who was the manager?**
    a) Steve Staunton b) Jack Charlton c) Martin O'Neil
    d) Mick McCarthy

Answers: Page 77

FUN FACTS, STORIES AND STATS

1. In the opening match of the 1996/97 season, David Beckham scored an incredible goal against Wimbledon. In the 87th minute, with United leading 2-0, he struck an audacious shot from within his own half. The ball perfectly lobbed Neil Sullivan and as Beckham cooly raised his arms in celebration, a superstar was born.

2. David Beckham was the poster boy of the Premier League and was affectionately known as "Golden Balls," After marrying Spice Girl Victoria "Posh and Becks" became a global celebrity power couple. His commitments off the pitch did not sit well with Sir Alex Ferguson. After a few heated incidences, most famously when Fergie kicked a boot at his head, he left Manchester United after 394 appearances to join Real Madrid's Galacticos in 2003.

3. Paul Ince "The Governor" played 281 times in the heart of the Manchester United midfield between 1989 and 1995 and helped the club win two Premier League titles, two FA Cups, a League Cup, a European Cup Winners' Cup, and a European Super Cup. Ince was the first black player to captain the England national side. A superstitious man, he would only put his shirt on as he entered the pitch. He eventually left the club to play for Italian giants Inter Milan.

4. Scottish international Pat Grerand played for Man United between 1963 and 1971. He won the first division title twice, the FA Cup and European Cup. Playing as a holding midfielder, his stability, consistency and passing accuracy were key to the club's success and he assisted numerous goals for teammates like Denis Law, George Best and Bobby Charlton.

5. David Beckham holds the record for the most free-kick goals scored in the Premier League with a total of 18. Fittingly, his last goal for the club was a free-kick, against Everton.

6. In the 1960s, Norbert "Nobby" Stiles was a rock in the United midfield. He was relentless defensive midfielder who played with intelligence and tanacity. He made 394 appearances for the club between 1960 and 1971. His greatest performance was in the 1968 European Cup final where he marked Benfica's Portuguese legend Eusébio out of the game. Suppressing the European Golden Boot winning forward helped the team win the match 4-1 after extra time. Stiles was a legend at international level too, lifting the World Cup with England in 1966.

7. Roy Keane holds the record for the highest number of red cards in English Football history, with 13.

8. in 2014 United smashed the British transfer record to bringing Angel di Maria to Old Trafford. However Louis van Gaal's style of management meant that he struggled to play with his usual creativity. The frustration boiled over after spending two months on the bench and in 2015, just a year after signing, he left to Paris Saint-Germain.

9. Owen Hargreaves impressed Sir Alex Ferguson so much during his time at Bayern Munich that he was willing to take a hige risk in signing the injury-prone midfielder. Dispite having missed most of the 2006/07 season with Bayern after suffering a broken leg, he joined the club in the summer of 2007 for £17 million. It initially proved to be a good move after a decent first season which included scoring in the penalty-shootout in the 2008 Champions League final victory over Chelsea. However he would only manage five more appearances for the club due to a string of injuries. His left the club in 2011 and retired in 2012 at the age of 31.

10. Beckham was a style icon and as well as having various different hairstyles he also helped bring tattoos back into fashion. He has 99 tattooed on his finger. That was the year he married Victoria, had his first child, Brooklyn, and helped United win a famous Treble.

TRIVIA QUIZ ANSWERS
Chapter 6: Midfield Masters - Part 1

MIDFIELDERS - PART 1
1. a) Portugal
2. a) Spoting Lisbon
3. a) Luke Chadwick
4. b) Quinton Fortune
5. a) 1992
6. d) Roma
7. b) Aston Villa
8. c) 1989
9. d) Norman Whiteside
10. c) Denmark

DAVID BECKHAM
1. b) Wimbledon
2. b) Galatasaray
3. c) Diego Simeone
4. b) Greece
5. d) FIFA World Club Cup
6. c) Kicked a boot at him
7. c) 59
8. b) Rivaldo
9. c) 18
10. c) PSG

PAUL INCE
1. c) The Guvnor
2. d) West Ham United
3. c) European Cup Winners' Cup
4. c) 1992–93
5. a) Inter Milan
6. a) 0
7. b) Captain England
8. a) They were scored in the same game
9. d) Puts his shirt on as he enters the pitch
10. d) Macclesfield Town

LEE SHARPE
1. b) Torquay United
2. a) PFA Young Player of the Year
3. d) 8
4. d) His fan club
5. d) Barcelona
6. a) Iceland
7. b) Bradford City
8. a) Coronation Street
9. d) Golf
10. d) My Idea of Fun

ROY KEANE
1. b) Cork
2. c) 1993
3. d) Nottingham Forest
4. b) 11
5. c) Eric Cantona
6. b) Juventus
7. b) Patrick Viera
8. b) Celtic
9. d) Sunderland
10. c) Martin O'Neil

PAUL SCHOLES

Chapter 7

MIDFIELD MASTERS
PART 2

MIDFIELDERS
PART 2

1. Which former player managed Northern Ireland from 2000-2003?
   a) Roy Keane b) Sammy McIlroy c) Mal Donaghy d) Keith Gillespie

2. Nobby Stiles danced around Wembley after the 1966 World Cup final with the trophy in one hand and what in the other?
   a) His boots b) His glasses c) A corner flag d) His false teeth

3. Which midfielder signed in the 1990s now runs a pizzeria?
   a) Jesper Blomqvist b) Jordi Cruyff c) Ben Thornley
   d) Andrei Kanchelskis

4. Which player said in his autobiography that the only player he could not get past was Park Ji-Sung?
   a) Zinedine Zidane b) Patrick Vieria c) Kaka d) Andrea Pirlo

5. Park Ji-Sung scored 5 of his 28 United against which opponent?
   a) Liverpool b) Chelsea c) Arsenal d) Manchester City

6. Bruno Fernandes was the club's top scorer in 2020-21 with how many goals in all competitions?
   a) 22 b) 24 c) 26 d) 28

7. Which two players made up an unorthodox central midfield partnership in the 2006 League Cup final?
   a) Ryan Giggs & John O'Shea b) Cristiano Ronaldo & Wes Brown
   c) Wayne Rooney & Nemanja Vidic
   d) Kieran Richardson & Mikael Silvestre

8. Which former teammate of the Class of '92 signed for Salford City in 2020?
   a) Fraizer Campbell b) Darron Gibson c) Chris Eagles d) Bojan Djordjic

9. Which winger was top scorer from 1976 to 1978?
   a) Steve Coppell b) Gordon Hill c) Brian Greenhoff d) Lou Macari

10. Juan Sebastian Veron won league titles in Argentina, England and where else?
    a) Spain b) Italy c) Portugal d) Qatar

Answers: Page 87

CRISTIANO RONALDO

1. **In which part of Portugal was Ronaldo born?**
   a) Porto b) Lagos c) Lisbon d) Madeira

2. **What happened to Ronaldo when he was 15 years old?**
   a) He fell out of a window b) He had heart surgery
   c) He was arrested d) He broke his shin bone

3. **Ronaldo became the most expensive teenager in English football history when, at 18 years old, United bought him from which Portuguese club for £12.24 million?**
   a) Benfica b) FC Porto c) Sporting Lisbon d) S.C Braga

4. **In what year did Ronaldo win his first Ballon d'Or?**
   a) 2007 b) 2008 c) 2010 d) 2011

5. **From which Italian club did Manchester United re-sign Ronaldo in 2021?**
   a) Inter Milan b) AC Milan c) Juventus d) Lazio

6. **Against which club did Ronaldo score twice on his second debut for United at Old Trafford in 2021?**
   a) Leeds b) Aston Villa c) Burnley d) Newcastle United

7. **As of 2023, Ronaldo is the all-time leading scorer in UEFA club competitions, how many goals has he scored?**
   a) 115 b) 132 c) 145 d) 162

8. **During his second spell at United he played 40 Premier league matches. How many goals did he score?**
   a) 15 b) 19 c) 22 d) 25

9. **As of 2023, Ronaldo is the joint most-capped international player. How many games has he played or Portugal?**
   a) 178 b) 189 c) 197 d) 206

10. **He has also scored the most international goals. With 122 in total. Which country has he scored the most against, with at total of 11?**
    a) Sweden b) Lithuania c) Luxembourg d) Hungary

Answers: Page 87

PAUL SCHOLES

1. **Where was Paul Scholes born?**
    a) Salford b) Oldham c) Stockport d) Bolton

2. **In which year did Scholes make his first team debut for Man United?**
    a) 1992 b) 1993 c) 1994 d) 1995

3. **Who said "He's almost untouchable in what he does. I never tire of watching him play. You rarely come across the complete footballer, but Scholes is as close to it as you can get."**
    a) David Beckham b) Alex Ferguson c) Jose Mourinho
    d) Zinedine Zidane

4. **Against which team did Scholes score the most goals, with 11?**
    a) Newcastle b) Liverpool c) Chelsea d) Aston Villa

5. **Scholes missed the 1999 Champions League final because he committed a foul on which Juventus player in the semi-final?**
    a) Zinedine Zidane b) Didier Deschamps c) Edgar Davids
    d) Gianluca Pessotto

6. **In his 499 Premier League matches, how many yellow cards did he receive?**
    a) 73 b) 85 c) 97 d) 108

7. **Scholes made his England debut in 1997 in a 2-1 win over South Africa. Which stadium was the game played in?**
    a) Wembley b) Villa Park c) Old Trafford d) St James's Park

8. **How many Premier League titles did Scholes win at United?**
    a) 9 b) 10 c) 11 d) 13

9. **Scholes became the first and last England player to be sent off in an international match at the old Wembley Stadium. Against which team was it?**
    a) Sweden b) Poland c) Denmark d) Finland

10. **For 31 days in 2019, Scholes was manager of which club that he supported as a child?**
    a) Stockport County b) Wigan Athletic c) Bury d) Oldham Athletic

Answers: Page 87

ANDREI KANCHELSKIS

1. **Which country was Kanchelskis born in?**
   a) Russia b) Ukraine c) Georgia d) Belarus

2. **And which country did he win 36 caps for?**
   a) Slovenia b) Russia c) Kazakhstan d) Bulgaria

3. **What year did Andrei Kanchelskis join Manchester United?**
   a) 1989 b) 1990 c) 1991 d) 1992

4. **From which club did United sign him for £650,000?**
   a) Spartak Moscow b) Dynamo Kyiv c) Hertha Berlin
    d) Shakhtar Donetsk

5. **What was the first trophy that he won for United?**
   a) FA Cup b) League Cup c) UEFA Super Cup
   d) UEFA Cup Winners' Cup

6. **Andrei Kanchelskis scored in three derby matches. Manchester, Merseyside, and which over?**
   a) Glasgow b) Milan c) Rome d) Belgrade

7. **In which cup final was he sent off for deliberate handball?**
   a) 1992 League Cup final b) 1994 League Cup final
   c) 1994 FA Cup final d) 1995 FA Cup final

8. **Kanchelskis left in 1995 to join which club?**
   a) Everton b) Fiorentina c) Rangers d) Manchester City

9. **For which team did he make two appearances in 2002–03, his last season in England football?**
   a) Manchester City b) Southampton c) Ipswich Town
   d) Birmingham City

10. **From 2018–2020, Kanchelskis managed Navbahor Namangan, a club playing in which country?**
    a) India b) Azerbaijan c) Israel d) Uzbekistan

Answers: Page 87

STEVE COPPELL

1. **In which UK city was Steve Coppell born?**
   a) London b) Leeds c) Liverpool d) Newcastle

2. **Before signing for Manchester United, he studied for a university degree in which subject?**
   a) Economics b) Law c) Geography d) English Literature

3. **What position did Coppell play?**
   a) Right back b) Left winger c) Right winger d) Utility player

4. **He won two FA Cups for United, but how many times was he a losing finalist?**
   a) 0 b) 1 c) 2 d) 3

5. **What did United win during Coppell's first season at Old Trafford?**
   a) FA Cup b) Anglo-Italian Cup c) Charity Shield d) Second Division

6. **A knee injury forced Coppell to retire at what age?**
   a) 24 b) 26 c) 28 d) 30

7. **Which team did he manage in the 1990 FA Cup final against Manchester United?**
   a) Crystal Palace b) Everton c) Brighton d) Sheffield Wednesday

8. **Coppell hold a club record that is unlikely to be broken. During his four years at United he set the record for the most consecutive games played for Manchester United. How many games was it?**
   a) 71 b) 105 c) 152 d) 207

9. **He was voted LMA Manager of the Year twice in succession in the mid-2000s when managing which club?**
   a) Bristol City b) Portsmouth c) Brentford d) Reading

10. **From 2016 to 2019 he managed three different clubs in which country?**
    a) Thailand b) India c) Australia d) Qatar

Answers: Page 87

FUN FACTS, STORIES AND STATS

1. Manchester United's third-highest appearance maker is Paul Scholes with 718 appearances and 155 goals. With his incredible passing ability and scoring ability, the brilliant play-making midfielder is regarded within the game as one of the best midfielders of his generation.

2. Paul Scholes was also famous for his bad tackles as well as his skills. He received a club record of 97 yellow cards and 4 red cards in his Premier League career.

3. Paul Scholes originally retired from football in May, 2011, however in 2012 there was an injury crisis in the club's midfield so he came out of retirement to help the club in its time of need. His number 18 shirt had been given to Ashley Young so he wore the number 22 shirt this time around. In his first game back, he scored against Bolton Wanderers. He eventually retired for good at the end of the 2013 season.

4. On his 19th birthday, Bryan Kidd scored at Wemblely stadium in the club's 4-1 European Cup final victory against Benfica in 1968. He played for both Man Utd and City and was also the assistant manager for both teams too.

5. Steve Coppell was devastating for opposing defenders. He was rapid down the wing, skilled on the ball and a deadly finisher. He played for United between 1975 and 1983 and scored 70 goals. He helped the team lift the 1977 FA Cup.

6. Antonio Valencia's ten-year stint at Old Trafford established him as one of the greatest Ecuadorian players of all time. He made 339 appearances for the club, captaining the side in his final season. He won two Premier League titles, an FA Cup, two League Cups, three FA Community Shields and the Europa League.

7. Ronaldo joined the club from Sporting Lisbon as an 18 year old in 2003. At the time he most expensive teenager in English football history. His best season as a United player came during 2007-08 campaign when he scored 42 goals in 49 games and led the team to Premier League and Champions League glory. In 2008 he won the first of his 5 Ballon d'Ors. In 2009, after 292 games and 118 goals, he left to join Real Madrid in a deal worth £80 million.

8. In the 2007-08 season, Ronaldo broke the record for the highest number of Premier League goals scored in a season for Manchester United. He scored 31 goals in 38 matches, helping United lift their tenth Premier League trophy.

9. Ronaldo rejoined Manchester United in 2021, scoring twice of his second debut against Newcastle. In his second period at the club he scored 27 goals in 54 games. This time he left on a controversially sour note after a tell-all interview with Piers Morgan. He gave a damming review of the club and aired his frustration at the lack of progress made by the club since Sir Alex Ferguson's departure. He moved to the Saudi Arabian team Al-Nassr where his annual salary is £177m

10. Born in Belfast, Norman Whiteside was a footballing prodigy. When he initially signed for the club, the youngster remained in Belfast, only flying to Manchester for training at the weekends. He made his debut as a 16 against Brighton and Hove Albion. He became the youngest player since Pele to play in a World Cup when he represented Northern Ireland in the 1982 finals at just 17 years and 40 days old. He is also the youngest player to score in both the League Cup and FA Cup finals. His career was cut short when he was forced to retire at the age of 26 due to an injury.

TRIVIA QUIZ ANSWERS
Chapter 7: Midfield Masters - Part 2

MIDFIELDERS - PART 2
1. b) Sammy McIlroy
2. d) His false teeth
3. a) Jesper Blomqvist
4. d) Andrea Pirlo
5. c) Arsenal
6. d) 28
7. a) Ryan Giggs & John O'Shea
8. b) Darron Gibson
9. b) Gordon Hill
10. b) Italy

CRISTIANO RONALDO
1. d) Madeira
2. b) He had heart surgery
3. c) Sporting Lisbon
4. b) 2008
5. c) Juventus
6. d) Newcastle United
7. c) 145
8. b) 19
9. c) 197
10. c) Luxembourg

PAUL SCHOLES
1. a) Salford
2. c) 1994
3. d) Zinedine Zidane
4. a) Newcastle
5. b) Didier Deschamps
6. c) 97
7. c) Old Trafford
8. c) 11
9. a) Sweden
10. d) Oldham Athletic

ANDREI KANCHELSKIS
1. b) Ukraine
2. b) Russia
3. c) 1991
4. d) Shakhtar Donetsk
5. c) UEFA Super Cup
6. a) Glasgow
7. b) 1994 League Cup final
8. a) Everton
9. b) Southampton
10. d) Uzbekistan

STEVE COPPELL
1. c) Liverpool
2. a) Economics
3. c) Right winger
4. c) 2
5. d) Second Division
6. c) 28
7. a) Crystal Palace
8. d) 207
9. d) Reading
10. b) India

Chapter 8
MIDFIELD MASTERS
PART 3

MIDFIELDERS
PART 3

1. Brazilian Casemiro signed from which club in 2022?
    a) Barcelona b) Real Madrid c) Juventus d) São Paulo

2. Which player took 11 penalties during the 2018/19 season?
    a) Fred b) Paul Pogba c) Alexis Sánchez d) Marcus Rashford

3. How many did he score?
    a) 6 b) 8 c) 9 d) 11

4. How many appearances did Owen Hargreaves make during his four injury-plagued seasons at Old Trafford?
    a) 28 b) 33 c) 39 d) 46

5. In 2003, who became the first Brazilian to play for United?
    a) Kleberson b) Anderson c) Fabio Da Silva d) Rodrigo Possebon

6. Bruno Fernandes and Nani both signed from which Portuguese club?
    a) FC Porto b) FC Braga c) Benfica d) Sporting Lisbon

7. Which midfielder has taken the most penalties for the club in the Premier League?
    a) Bruno Fernandes b) Paul Scholes c) Paul Pogba
    d) David Beckham

8. What happened to Christian Eriksen whilst playing for Denmark at Euro 2020
    a) A cardiac arrest b) A broken skull c) A broken ankle d) A stroke

9. During the 2018/19 season Paul Pogba took 11 penalties. How many did he score?
    a) 7 b) 8 c) 9 d) 10

10. Who scored the first Premier League goal at Old Trafford?
    a) Gary Speed b) Vinnie Jones c) Darren Anderton d) Peter Beardsley

Answers: Page 97

GEORGE BEST

1. Where in Ireland was George Best born?
   a) Cork   b) Dublin   c) Belfast   d) Derry

2. What age did Best make his debut for Manchester United, on September 4th, 1963 in a 1-0 victory against West Bromwich Albion at Old Trafford?
   a) 15   b) 16   c) 17   d) 18

3. For how many consecutive seasons was Best the top goalscorer for the club?
   a) 5   b) 6   c) 7   d) 8

4. After a European Cup quarter-final win against Benfica in March 1966, the Portuguese media nicknamed him what?
   a) The Belfast baller   b) The king of Old Trafford   c) King George
   d) The fifth Beatle

5. By what age had George Best won the First division, European Cup and the Ballon d'Or?
   a) 20   b) 21   c) 22   d) 23

6. Best once scored how many goals in an 8-2 FA Cup victory against Northampton Town?
   a) 4   b) 5   c) 6   d) 7

7. Best made 470 appearances for United, scoring how many goals?
   a) 150   b) 179   c) 201   d) 239

8. During the 60s and 70s, he starred in commercials for what?
   a) Cigarettes   b) Whiskey   c) Sausages   d) Hair gel

9. Which leagues did Best NOT play for after he left Manchester United?
   a) Kong First Division   b) North American Soccer League
   c) League of Ireland   d) Scottish second division

10. What's the title of George Best's autobiography?
    a) Best of times   b) Scored!   c) Good, Better, Best
    d) The good, the bad and the bubbly

   Answers: Page 97

RYAN GIGGS

1. Originally Ryan's surname wasn't Giggs. What was it?
   a) Wilson b) Jones c) Evans d) Hancock

2. His father was a professional what?
   a) Golfer b) Rugby player c) Dancer d) Gymnast

3. Against which club did Giggs make his debut in a 2-0 loss at Old Trafford?
   a) Liverpool b) Everton c) Arsenal d) Manchester City

4. Giggs spent time at which club as a schoolboy footballer?
   a) Manchester City b) Liverpool c) Everton d) Blackburn Rovers

5. In the 1998-99 FA Cup semi-final replay, Ryan famously score a wonder goal against which team?
   a) Tottenham Hotspur b) Chelsea c) Aston Villa d) Arsenal

6. As of 2023, Giggs holds the record for the most assists in the Premier League. 51 more than the next player. How many?
   a) 111 b) 130 c) 162 d) 198

7. How many times was Giggs sent off for Manchester United?
   a) 0 b) 2 c) 6 d) 9

8. Ryan Giggs has won more English League titles than any other player. How many has he won?
   a) 9 b) 11 c) 13 d) 15

9. Giggs won the BBC sports personality of the year award in which year?
   a) 1999 b) 2001 c) 2008 d) 2009

10. Giggs was a one-club player. How many years did he play in the Manchester United first team?
    a) 19 b) 21 c) 23 d) 25

Answers: Page 97

DUNCAN EDWARDS

1. Duncan Edwards was born in which midlands town in the UK?
   a) Dudley b) Walsall c) Burton-on-Trent d) Wolverhampton

2. Edwards made his Manchester United debut on 4th April, 1953 against Cardiff City. What age was he?
   a) 15 b) 16 c) 17 d) 18

3. Which of these was not one of his nicknames?
   a) The Tank b) Boom Boom c) The Eagle d) Big Dunc

4. What position did he play?
   a) Left winger b) Left half c) Centre forward d) Full back

5. How many First Division titles did he win?
   a) 0 b) 1 c) 2 d) 3

6. How many caps did he receive for England before his tragic death aged 21?
   a) 9 b) 12 c) 15 d) 18

7. His England debut came in a 7:2 win against which nation?
   a) Wales b) Portugal c) Denmark d) Scotland

8. He was the youngest player to play for England until who broke his record?
   a) Wayne Rooney b) Michael Owen c) Paul Gascoigne
   d) Theo Walcott

9. Who said this about Edwards? "I always felt I could compare well with any player - except Duncan. He was such a talent, I always felt inferior to him."
   a) Jackie Blanchflower b) Bobby Charlton c) Dennis Violett
   d) Bill Foulkes

10. He was played by actor Sam Claflin in a 2011 film about the Munich disaster called what?
    a) United b) Babes c) Manchester's Finest d) Busby's babes

Answers: Page 97

BRYAN ROBSON

1. What year did Robson sign for Manchester United debut, for a then British record transfer fee of £1.5 million?
    a) 1980   b) 1981   c) 1982   d) 1983

2. He made 198 appearances for which club before joining United?
    a) Carlisle United   b) West Brom   c) Newcastle   d) Port Vale

3. Which manager signed him?
    a) Tommy Docherty   b) Dave Sexton   c) Ron Atkinson
    d) Sir Alex Ferguson

4. For how many years was Robson captain of Manchester United?
    a) 8   b) 10   c) 12   d) 14

5. Robson made 90 appearances for England. How many of those games was he the captain for?
    a) 45   b) 55   c) 65   d) 75

6. How many appearances did Robson make for Manchester United?
    a) 386   b) 432   c) 461   d) 492

7. How many goals did he score?
    a) 89   b) 99   c) 109   d) 119

8. Which club did Robson leave United to join? A club he would later go to manage?
    a) Middlesbrough   b) Fulham   c) Newcastle   d) Stoke City

9. Which national team did he manage?
    a) Thailand   b) Japan   c) South Korea   d) China

10. Robson returned to the club in 2008 to work in what role?
    a) Youth team coach   b) Assistant Manager   c) Ambassador
    d) Reserve team coach

Answers: Page 97

FUN FACTS, STORIES AND STATS

1. Ryan Giggs has a medal for each of Manchester United's 13 Premier League titles. He is the only player to play in the first 22 Premier League seasons. He is also the only player to score in the first 21 seasons.

2. During the Swinging Sixties Northern Ireland's George Best was as famous for his pace, skill, balance and two-footed dribbling skills on the pitch, as he was for his international playboy lifestyle off it. Nicknamed the "The fifth Beatle", he won the First Division, European Cup and the Ballon d'Or y the tender age of 22. Life in the fast lane eventually caught up with him and he died at the age of 59 after complications from a liver transplant.

3. Nicky Butt made 387 appearances between 1992 to 2004. In that time he helped the team win six Premier League titles, three FA Cups, a UEFA Champions League, and an Intercontinental Cup. In 2012 he returned to Old Trafford to coach the reserve team. Four years later he became the head coach of the youth academy.

4. Duncan Edwards was only 21 when he died in the Munich air disater. Very little footage of him remains which makes it almost impossible to determine just how good he was. Sir Matt Busby, described him as "the most complete player in Britain, and possibly the world." His close friend and teammate Bobby Charlton said he was "the best player I have ever seen. The best player I played with, for United or England." Edwards was dynamic, powerful, two-footed and had a range of passing that few have ever matched. He made his United debut at 17 and at the time of his death, he had already made 177 appearances, scoring 21 goals. He'd also played 18 games for England. At his funeral someone said "His talent, even genius, we will see again. But there will only ever be one Duncan Edwards."

5. The Geordie winger George Wall played a key part in Manchester United's first great team of the early 1900s. He scored 19 goals as United won their first ever league title in 1908. He also scored in the first ever Charity Shield match as United beat QPR 4-0.

6. Michael Carrick was signed from Spurs for £18.6 million, which at the time was big money. He proved to be worth every penny as he went on to win 17 major titles with United. He was a vital part of the midfield engine and could also step back into defence when required and always seemed in control even in the highest-pressure games.

7. Paddy Crerand was a combative, hard-tackling midfielder, who was integral to the club's success mid-1960s. A precise passer who never stopped running, he did the unglamorous work so the superstars up front could shine. A Red Devil through and through, he was a regular on the club's TV station MUTV.

8. Scotsman Lou Macari made 400 appearances for United scoring 97 goals. He began his career playing in attack, before moving into midfield. He was part of the club's 1974 relegation but stayed at the club and helped lead them back into the First Division the following season.

9. Argentine Juan Sebastián Verón joined United from Lazio in 2001 for what was at the time a British record transfer fee of £28.1 million.He had trouble adapting to the relentless pace of the league and his performances didn't quite match the price tag. A series of injuries didn't help his casue and he was eventually sold to Roman Abramovic's Chelsea in 2003.

10. The Northern Irish winger Sammy MacIlroy was Matt Busby's final signing for Manchester United when he joined in 1971 as a 17-year-old. He instantly endeared himself to the United fans in a memorable debut in the Manchester Derby, scoring once and assisting twice at Maine Road. Sammy was an integral part of the side in the 1970s, reaching three FA Cup finals in 4 years. He suffered defeats to Southampton and Arsenal in 1976 and 1979 but helped United beat Liverpool 2-1 in 1977, winning the only major honour of his 11-year career at the club.

TRIVIA QUIZ ANSWERS
Chapter 8: Midfield Masters - Part 3

MIDFIELDERS - PART 3
1. b) Real Madrid
2. b) Paul Pogba
3. b) 8
4. c) 39
5. a) Kleberson
6. d) Sporting Lisbon
7. a) Bruno Fernandes
8. a) A cardiac arrest
9. b) 8
10. d) Peter Beardsley

GEORGE BEST
1. c) Belfast
2. c) 17
3. b) 6
4. d) The fifth Beatle
5. c) 22
6. c) 6
7. b) 179
8. c) Sausages
9. d) Scottish second division
10. d) The good, the bad and the bubbly

RYAN GIGGS
1. a) Wilson
2. b) Rugby player
3. b) Everton
4. a) Manchester City
5. d) Arsenal
6. c) 162
7. a) 0
8. c) 13
9. d) 2009
10. c) 23

DUNCAN EDWARDS
1. a) Dudley
2. b) 16
3. c) The Eagle
4. b) Left half
5. c) 2
6. d) 18
7. d) Scotland
8. b) Michael Owen
9. b) Bobby Charlton
10. a) United

BRYAN ROBSON
1. b) 1981
2. b) West Brom
3. c) Ron Atkinson
4. c) 12
5. c) 65
6. c) 461
7. b) 99
8. a) Middlesbrough
9. a) Thailand
10. c) Ambassador

Chapter 9
FANTASTIC FORWARDS
PART 1

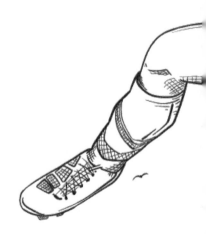

STRIKERS
PART 1

1. Who scored the winning goal in the 1990 FA Cup semi-final replay and is widely credited with saving Sir Alex Ferguson's job?
   a) Mark Hughes b) Mark Robins c) Brian McClair d) Danny Wallace

2. Which forward was known as Jaws due to his lack of front teeth?
   a) Brian McClair b) Joe Jordan c) Andy Ritchie d) Jimmy Greenhoff

3. Brian McClair scored the only goal in which of these matches?
   a) 1991 Cup Winners' Cup final b) 1991 Super Cup
   c) 1992 League Cup final d) 1996 FA Cup final

4. Which Manchester United striker had claimed he would never sign for United before eventually doing so?
   a) Louis Saha b) Eric Cantona c) Alan Smith d) Diego Forlan

5. Who was part of the Arsenal team that beat United in the 1979 FA Cup final before winning the cup with United in 1983 and 1985?
   a) Mark Hughes b) Norman Whiteside c) Jimmy Greenhoff
   d) Frank Stapleton

6. Carlos Tevez spent two seasons on loan at United from which club?
   a) Corinthians b) Boca Juniors c) West Ham United
   d) Manchester City

7. How many goals did Alexis Sanchez score for United in 45 appearances?
   a) 2 b) 5 c) 8 d) 11

8. Federico Macheda announced himself to the world in 2009 by scoring a last-minute winner against which club?
   a) Aston Villa b) Newcastle United c) Portsmouth d) QPR

9. Which member of the Busby Babes went on to win two England caps and manage in the United States?
   a) Ernie Taylor b) Johnny Berry c) Dennis Violett d) Albert Scanlon

10. Anthony Martial joined United from which club?
    a) Toulouse b) Monaco c) Lyon d) Sochaux

Answers: Page 107

WAYNE ROONEY

1. In October 2002, Rooney shot to stardom as a 16 year-old after scoring a wonder goal for Everton against which club?
   a) Newcastle b) Arsenal c) Chelsea d) Liverpool

2. He signed for United in 2004 for a then, world-record transfer fee for a teenager. How much did he sign for?
   a) £18.7 million b) £21.7 million c) £25.6 million d) £29.5 million

3. Rooney scored a hat trick on his debut against which team in the Champions League?
   a) PSV Eindhoven b) Fenerbahce c) Benfica d) Bayern Munich

4. Rooney became the youngest player to play for England when he earned his first cap at what age?
   a) 16 b) 17 c) 18 d) 19

5. Rooney holds the record as the most capped outfield player for England. How many games did he play for his country?
   a) 111 b) 120 c) 123 d) 129

6. How many goals did he score for his country?
   a) 39 b) 45 c) 53 d) 59

7. Rooney is Manchester United's leading goalscorer with 253 goals in 559 appearances. How many hat tricks did he score for the club?
   a) 4 b) 5 c) 8 c) 11

8. Rooney has a tattoo on his arm saying what?
   a) Just enough education to perform b) Get rich or die trying
   c) I get by with a little help from my friends
   d) You'll never walk alone

9. How many major trophies did he win during his thirteen years at the club?
   a) 8 b) 11 b) 13 d) 18

10. Rooney finished his playing career at which club?
    a) LA Galaxy b) Everton c) DC United d) Derby County

Answers: Page 107

ANDY COLE

1. Andy Cole was born in Nottingham but began his career with which London club?
   a) Arsenal b) Crystal Palace c) Dulwich Hamlet d) Leyton Orient

2. When Cole was bought from Newcastle United in 1995, the fee was £6 million, plus which player?
   a) Paul Parker b) Lee Sharpe c) Simon Davies d) Keith Gillespie

3. Cole scored five goals in United's 9-0 win over which opponents, less than two months after joining the club?
   a) Bolton Wanderers b) Ipswich Town c) Swindon Town
   d) Crystal Palace

4. He had a long-time feud with which Manchester United teammate?
   a) Teddy Sheringham b) Roy Keane c) Phil Neville d) Nicky Butt

5. Who broke both Cole's legs in a reserve team match between United Liverpool in 1996?
   a) John Scales b) Stan Collymore c) Rob Jones d) Neil Ruddock

6. How many Premier League goals did he score over his career?
   a) 124 b) 146 c) 169 d) 187

7. Cole was capped only 15 times for England and scored once, against which nation?
   a) Georgia b) Estonia c) Malta d) Albania

8. Which was the only season Cole finished as top scorer, in the league and in all competitions?
   a) 1995-96 b) 1997-98 c) 1998-99 d) 2000-01

9. In 1999, Cole released a cover of a Gap Band song which reached number 68 in the UK Singles Chart, what was the name of the song?
   a) Something Extra b) Outstanding c) Strange People d) Unbroken

10. Cole played for 12 English clubs in total, which of these did he play for before his time at United?
    a) Bristol City b) Portsmouth c) Birmingham City
    d) Nottingham Forest

Answers: Page 107

DWIGHT YORKE

1. **Yorke played 72 times for which nation?**
   a) Jamaica b) Barbados c) Grenada d) Trinidad & Tobago

2. **He represented his nation at which World Cup?**
   a) 1998 b) 2002 c) 2006 d) 2010

3. **Before joining Manchester United, he had spent eight years at which club?**
   a) Bolton Wanderers b) Aston Villa c) Norwich City d) Celtic

4. **He was joint-top scorer with 8 goals in the 1998/99 Champions League with which player?**
   a) Stefan Effenberg b) Filippo Inzaghi c) Andriy Shevchenko
   d) Nuno Gomes

5. **He won the Premier League Golden Boot in which of his seasons with United?**
   a) 1998/99 b) 1999/00 c) 2000/01 d) 2001/02

6. **How many hat-tricks did Yorke score for Manchester United?**
   a) 1 b) 2 c) 3 d) 4

7. **Yorke left Manchester United in 2002 and linked up with strike partner Andy Cole again at which club?**
   a) Blackburn Rovers b) Birmingham City c) Sunderland
   d) Aston Villa

8. **He was the first non-European to enter the Premier League 100 club, how many in total did he score in the league?**
   a) 103 b) 109 c) 116 d) 123

9. **What is the name of Yorke's autobiography, released in 2009?**
   a) Caribbean Kid b) Born to Score c) Always Dwight
   d) Smiling Assassin

10. **He guided which club to the 2022 Australian Cup?**
    a) Melbourne Victory b) Perth Glory c) Sydney FC d) Macarthur FC

Answers: Page 107

ERIC CANTONA

1. **In which French City was Cantona born on 24 May, 1966?**
   a) Paris b) Marseille c) Toulouse d) Monaco

2. **Cantona grew up living in what?**
   a) A cave b) A canal boat c) Army barracks d) A treehouse

3. **Which club did Cantona begin his professional career at?**
   a) PSG b) Auxerre c) Olympique de Marseille d) Lyon

4. **His career paused in 1984 because of what?**
   a) A 12-month ban b) A broken leg c) He was in prison d) National service

5. **Which club did Manchester United sign Cantona from?**
   a) Liverpool b) Leeds United c) Sheffield United d) PSG

6. **In 1993 Cantona was banned for 8 months for kung fu kicking an opposition fan of what team?**
   a) Wimbledon b) West Ham United c) Ipswich Town
   d) Crystal Palace

7. **How many premier league titles did Cantona win during his time at Manchester United?**
   a) 2 b) 3 c) 4 d) 5

8. **In 1998 Eric Cantona starred as the French ambassador, alongside Cate Blanchett, in which BAFTA award winning film?**
   a) Braveheart b) Elizabeth c) Shakespeare in Love
   d) Romeo and Juliet

9. **Manchester United Cantona's final club. How old was he when he retired?**
   a) 28 b) 30 c) 33 d) 35

10. **In 2011, which team made Cantona their Director of Soccer?**
    a) LA Galaxy b) New York red bulls c) New York Cosmos
    d) Inter Miami

Answers: Page 107

FUN FACTS, STORIES AND STATS

1. Wayne Rooney is Manchester United's leading goal scorer, with 253 goals in 559 appearances. Bobby Charlton held the record of 249 goals in 758 appearances for almost 45 years, until Rooney overtook him in January 2017.

2. Rooney is the third-highest scorer in Premier League history with 208 goals. Ahead of him are only Harry Kane and Alan Shearer.

3. At 17 years and 317 days old, Wayne Rooney became the youngest player to ever score for England. He scored in his sixth appearance for his country in a 2-1 Euro 2004 qualifier win against Macedonia in June 2003

4. In 1982 Northern Ireland's Norman Whiteside signed for the club at the age of 17. He became the youngest player to score a senior goal for Man United at 17 years and 8 days. He also holds the record for being the youngest player to feature at a World Cup at 17 years and 40 days. And the youngest player to score in a League Cup and FA Cup Final. He played 278 times for Man United and won the FA Cup twice before being sold to Everton in 1989. Unfortunately, he was forced to retire at just 26 years old due to a serious knee injury.

5. The Trinidad and Tobago international Dwight Yorke scored 123 Premier League goals in his career. The only non-European player to score more than him is Manchester City's, Sergio Aguero.

6. Dwight Yorke had an exceptional season as part of the famous treble winning team in 1998/99. Yorke scored 29 goals in all competitions that season, and he was the joint top goalscorer with Jimmy Floyd Hasselbaink and Michael Owen in the Premier League with 18 goals. He was also joint top goalscorer with Andriy Shevchenko in the Champions League with 8 goals.

7. Andy Cole had a hugely successful career at Manchester United but he also played for seven other clubs in the top tier of English football. He played for Arsenal, Manchester City, Blackburn Rovers, Fulham, Portsmouth, Sunderland and Newcastle United. He is the fourth-highest Premier League goalscorer with 187 goals.

8. Manchester United's most lethal trio in PL history was the Wayne Rooney (12), Carlos Tevez (14), and Cristiano Ronaldo (31) combo of 2007/08. They scored 57 goals within them.

9. Eric Cantona joined Man United from First Division champions Leeds United in 1992 and immediately helped the club win the inaugural Premier League title. His flamboyant arrogance made a lasting impression on a younger generation at the club, as they too went on to become superstars themselves. "King Eric," won two League and Cup doubles at United in 1993/94 and 1995/96. He retired from football in 1997 at the age of 30 having scored 82 goals in 185 games for the club.

10. Eric Cantona will perhaps always be best remembered for the infamous kung-fu kick he launched at a Crystal Palace fan during a heated Premier League match at Selhurst Park on January 25, 1995. Cantona had been red-carded for kicking Palace's defender Richard Shaw and as he was escorted off the pitch a Palace fan named Matthew Simmonds hurled abuse at him and Cantona flipped. He leapt over the advertising hoards and kung-fu kicked Simmons in the chest, then followed up with a punch. He was banned for nine months. What has become almost as famous as the kick itself is Cantona's two-sentence address at a press conference regarding the attack. The only words he spoke were, "When the seagulls follow the trawler, it's because they think sardines will be thrown into the sea. Thank you." These words have now gone down in football history and the whole affair remains one of the most extraordinary moments in British sport.

TRIVIA QUIZ ANSWERS
Chapter 9: Fantastic Forwards - Part 1

STRIKERS - PART 1

1. b) Mark Robins
2. b) Joe Jordan
3. b) 1991 Super Cup
4. c) Alan Smith
5. d) Frank Stapleton
6. c) West Ham United
7. b) 5
8. a) Aston Villa
9. c) Dennis Violett
10. b) Monaco

WAYNE ROONEY

1. b) Arsenal
2. c) £25.6 million
3. b) Fenerbahce
4. b) 17
5. b) 120
6. c) 53
7. c) 8
8. a) Just Enough Education to Perform
9. b) 13
10. d) Derby County

ERIC CANTONA

1. b) Marseille
2. a) A cave
3. c) Olympique de Marseille
4. d) National service
5. b) Leeds United
6. d) Crystal Palace
7. c) 4
8. b) Elizabeth
9. b) 30
10. c) New York Cosmos

ANDY COLE

1. a) Arsenal
2. d) Keith Gillespie
3. b) Ipswich Town
4. a) Teddy Sheringham
5. d) Neil Ruddock
6. d) 187
7. d) Albania
8. b) 1997-98
9. b) Outstanding
10. a) Bristol City

DWIGHT YORKE

1. d) Trinidad & Tobago
2. c) 2006
3. b) Aston Villa
4. c) Andriy Shevchenko
5. a) 1998-99
6. c) 3
7. a) Blackburn Rovers
8. d) 123
9. b) Born to Score
10. d) Macarthur FC

Bobby Charlton

Chapter 10
FANTASTIC FORWARDS
PART 2

STRIKERS
PART 2

1. **Which forward was the first winner and first two-time winner of the Sir Matt Busby Player of the Year?**
   a) Mark Hughes b) Brian McClair c) Eric Cantona
   d) Frank Stapleton

2. **Peter Davenport finished as top scorer in which season?**
   a) 1978-79 b) 1981-82 c) 1983-84 d) 1986-87

3. **Before signing for United in 2022, Antony played his club football for Ajax and who else?**
   a) São Paulo b) Corinthians c) Benfica d) Fluminense

4. **Which striker signed from Sunderland in 2003?**
   a) Louis Saha b) Daniel Nardiello c) Alan Smith d) David Bellion

5. **United's fastest hat-trick was scored by Ernie Goldthorpe in 1923 against Notts County. How long did it take?**
   a) 2 minutes b) 4 minutes c) 7 minutes d) 9 minutes

6. **Which striker scored the last Manchester United goal under Sir Alex Ferguson?**
   a) Robin van Persie b) Wayne Rooney c) Danny Welbeck
   d) Javier Hernandez

7. **Joe Spence scored 168 goals for United in a career spanning from 1919 until when?**
   a) 1928 b) 1933 c) 1936 d) 1939

8. **Who was the first player United paid more than £1 million for?**
   a) Mark Hughes b) Ian Storey-Moore c) Joe Jordan d) Gary Birtles

9. **Dimitar Berbatov scored 56 goals for Manchester United, which was the only club he scored more for?**
   a) CSKA Sofia b) Bayer Leverkusen c) Tottenham Hotspur d) Monaco

10. **In 2020, Marcus Rashford successfully led a campaign to change government policy on what issue?**
    a) Climate Change b) Homelessness c) Child Poverty
    d) Free Speech

Answers: Page 117

BOBBY CHARLTON

1. **What year was Bobby Charlton born?**
   a) 1934 b) 1935 c) 1936 d) 1937

2. **In which UK county was he born?**
   a) Durham b) Cumbria c) Northumberland d) North Yorkshire

3. **In what year did Bobby Charlton make his debut for Man United?**
   a) 1954 b) 1956 c) 1958 d) 1960

4. **What is the name of Bobby's brother who played alongside him in the 1966 World Cup winning team? He played for Leeds United and was manager of the Republic of Ireland.**
   a) James b) Jack c) Alex d) Martin

5. **He played for United for 17 years. How many games did he play?**
   a) 728 b) 758 c) 799 d) 827

6. **In which year did Bobby Charlton win the Ballon d'Or?**
   a) 1960 b) 1966 c) 1971 d) 1976

7. **In honour of the man, Manchester United named what after Sir Bobby Charlton?**
   a) The training ground b) A stand c) The dressing room
   d) A hospitality suite

8. **Charlton has made the most appearances in the FA Cup for Manchester United. How many times did he play in the competition?**
   a) 52 b) 63 c) 78 d) 87

9. **Which club did Charlton briefly play for after leaving Manchester United?**
   a) Bolton Wanderers b) Preston North End c) Burnley
   d) Sheffield United

10. **Charlton's record of scoring 49 goals for England stood for how many years before Wayne Rooney broke it?**
    a) 35 b) 40 c) 45 d) 50

Answers: Page 117

DENIS LAW

1. Which part of Scotland was Law born?
   a) Glasgow b) Aberdeen c) Edinburgh d) Stirling

2. He began his professional career at which club?
   a) Huddersfield Town b) Bolton Wanderers c) Stoke City
   d) West Brom

3. From which team did United sign Law?
   a) Aberdeen b) Celtic c) Man City d) Torino

4. At the time of signing, Law was a British record transfer fee of how much?
   a) £65,000 b) £98,000 c) £115,000 d) £134,000

5. In the 1963-64 season, Law set the record for the most goals scored by a United player, in all competitions.. How many goals did score?
   a) 43 b) 46 c) 49 d) 51

6. Which team did Law join upon leaving the club in 1974?
   a) Everton b) Liverpool c) Leeds United d) Manchester City

7. He played 55 times for Scotland. With Kenny Dalglish, he is the country's joint top goalscorer with how many goals?
   a) 20 b) 25 c) 30 d) 35

8. Law has scored the most FA Cup goals for the club with how many goals?
   a) 22 b) 34 c) 39 d) 46

9. What year did Law become the only Scottish player to win the Ballon d'Or?
   a)1964 b) 1966 c) 1968 d) 1970

10. Law made 404 appearances for United. How many goals did he score?
    a) 199 b) 215 c) 237 d) 267

Answers: Page 117

LOU MACARI

1. **What is Macari's full first name?**
   a) Louke b) Louis c) Laurence d) Luigi

2. **Macari joined Manchester United in 1973 from which club?**
   a) Rangers b) Aberdeen c) Celtic d) Hibernian

3. **United swooped in to sign Macari after Pat Crerand overheard which manager talking about signing him?**
   a) Brian Clough b) Don Revie c) Dave Sexton d) Bill Shankly

4. **Manchester United won the 1977 FA Cup final thanks to Macari's shot deflecting in off which teammate for the winning goal?**
   a) Steve Coppell b) Jimmy Nicholl c) Jimmy Greenhoff
   d) Sammy McIlroy

5. **He was twice the club's joint-top scorer in all competitions, but in which season did he score the most outright?**
   a) 1973-74 b) 1975-76 c) 1979-80 d) 1981-82

6. **How many caps did Macari win for Scotland?**
   a) 14 b) 24 c) 34 d) 44

7. **His first coaching role was as Player-Manager of which club?**
   a) Brentford b) Wrexham c) Brighton & Hove Albion
   d) Swindon Town

8. **As manager of Birmingham City and then Stoke City, Macari won which trophy in 1991 and 1992?**
   a) Full Members' Cup b) Football League Trophy
   c) Anglo-Italian Cup d) Second Division Play-Offs

9. **What does Macari own on Chester Road, close to Old Trafford?**
   a) A fish & chip shop b) A pub c) A coffee shop d) A butcher's

10. **In which city did he set up the Macari Centre to help with homelessness in 2016?**
    a) Bristol b) Glasgow c) Stoke-on-Trent d) Birmingham

Answers: Page 117

OLE GUNNER SOLSKJAER

1. Solskjaer signed for Manchester United in 1996 from which club?
   a) Rosenborg b) Lillestrøm c) Viking d) Molde

2. Solskjaer scored six minutes into his Manchester United debut against which club?
   a) Wimbledon b) Derby County c) Blackburn Rovers
   d) Middlesbrough

3. Often referred to as a "super-sub", how many of his 126 Manchester United goals were scored as a substitute?
   a) 28 b) 37 c) 46 d) 55

4. The most famous of those goals was the winner in the 1999 Champions League final. What time in the match was the goal scored at?
   a) 91:54 b) 92:17 c) 92:33 d) 93:01

5. Four more were those he scored in an 8-1 away win over Nottingham Forest, in which minute did he score his first?
   a) 72nd b) 75th c) 80th d) 82nd

6. Intensive knee surgery forced him to miss the entirety of which season?
   a) 2003-04 b) 2004-05 c) 2005-06 d) 2006-07

7. How many major international tournaments did he represent Norway in?
   a) 0 b) 1 c) 2 d) 3

8. In what year did he become Man United reserve team manager?
   a) 2008 b) 2009 c) 2011 d) 2012

9. With Solskjaer as manager, Manchester United lost the 2021 Europa League final to which team?
   a) Villarreal b) Sevilla c) Real Sociedad d) Valencia

10. He was manager of United for 127 Premier League games. How many of those did he win?
    a) 45 b) 59 c) 67 d) 78

Answers: Page 117

FUN FACTS, STORIES AND STATS

1. For 45 years Bobby Charlton held the record as England's highest-ever goalscorer with 49 goals in 106 appearances, until September 2018, when Wayne Rooney broke it. Rooney finished his international career with 53 goals in 120 appearances. He was the highest England goalscorer until Harry Kane overtook him in March 2023.

2. Scotland's Denis Law began his career with Huddersfield Town and Manchester City, then went out to Italy to play for Torino before coming back to Manchester, but this time with United. The original King of the Stretford End Law scored 237 goals in 398 appearance between 1962 and 1973. He is the joint top all-time scorer for Scotland, matching Kenny Dalglish, who took 102 caps to notch the same total. In 1964 Denis Law became the only Scottish footballer to win the Ballon d'Or award.

3. Denis Law holds the club record for the most goals scored in a season. During the 1963-64 season, he scored 46 goals in 42 games including 30 goals in 30 league appearances.

4. Nicknamed the "babyface assassin" Ole Gunnar Solskjaer built a reputation as a super substitute. He once scored four times in 13 minutes after coming off the bench against Nottingham Forest in the 1998-99 season.

5. Ole Gunnar Solskjaer's most famous substitute appearance came against Bayern Munich in the 1998-99 UEFA Champions League final when he came off the bench to score the winning goal in stoppage time to make it 2-1.

6. Stan Pearson and strike partner Jack Rowley had an almost telepathic understanding and between them, they scored 52 of the club's 95 goals during the 1952 title-winning season.

7. Belgian Romelu Lukaku signed for United for £75 million in 2017 after an impressive spell at Everton. He made 96 appearances for the club and scored 42 goals. However, after a breakdown in relations with the club, Lukaku left to join Inter Milan in 2019.

8. "Give it to Joe" was often chanted by the crowd whenever Joe Spence was on the pitch. Hi's scintillating pace down the wings made him one of the club's few true stars between the wars. During his 14 years at Old Trafford, he made 510 appearances and scored 168 goals. It's no wonder he was known locally as 'Mr Soccer'.

9. In July 2009, in a surprise move, Liverpool and England legend Michael Owen signed for Manchester United. He was handed the number 7 shirt after the departure of Cristiano Ronaldo to Real Madrid. He made 52 appearances for United and scored 17 goals before moving to Stoke City in 2012

10. The Scot Bryan McClair spent nearly 11 years at Manchester United and won 14 trophies including four Premier League titles. He was nicknamed "Choccy", because his last name rhymed with his favourite sweet, the chocolate éclair. McClair made 30 appearances for Scotland. After retiring he became a coach at Blackburn Rovers and then returned to Manchester United, where he spent several years as the Youth Academy Director.

TRIVIA QUIZ ANSWERS
Chapter 10: Fantastic Forwards - Part 2

STRIKERS - PART 2

1. b) Brian McClair
2. d) 1986-87
3. a) São Paulo
4. d) David Bellion
5. b) 4 minutes
6. d) Javier Hernandez
7. b) 1933
8. d) Gary Birtles
9. b) Bayer Leverkusen
10. c) Child Poverty

BOBBY CHARLTON

1. d) 1937
2. c) Northumberland
3. b) 1956
4. b) Jack
5. b) 758
6. b) 1966
7. b) A stand
8. c) 78
9. b) Preston North End
10. c) 45

DENIS LAW

1. b) Aberdeen
2. a) Huddersfield Town
3. d) Torino
4. c) £115,000
5. b) 46
6. d) Manchester City
7. c) 30
8. b) 34
9. a) 1964
10. c) 237

LOU MACARI

1. d) Luigi
2. c) Celtic
3. d) Bill Shankly
4. c) Jimmy Greenhoff
5. b) 1975-76
6. b) 24
7. d) Swindon Town
8. b) Football League Trophy
9. a) A fish & chip shop
10. c) Stoke-on-Trent

OLE GUNNER SOLSKJAER

1. d) Molde
2. c) Blackburn Rovers
3. a) 28
4. b) 92:17
5. c) 80th
6. b) 2004-05
7. c) 2
8. a) 2008
9. a) Villarreal
10. b) 59

Chapter 11

FANTASTIC FORWARDS
PART 3

Ruud van
Nistelrooy

STRIKERS
PART 3

1. Only three players have missed at least 10 penalties in the Premier League. Alan Shearer with 11, Wayne Rooney with 11, and who else with 10 misses?
   a) Teddy Sheringham b) Eric Cantona c) Paul Pogba
   d) Andy Cole

2. Wayne Rooney has scored the most penalties for Man Utd in the Premier League. How many has he scored?
   a) 15 b) 17 c) 20 d) 23

3. 17-year-old Federico Macheda burst onto the scene with a last-minute winner against which team in 2009?
   a) Aston Villa b) Everton c) Brighton d) Crystal Palace

4. Romelu Lukaku made 96 appearances, scoring how man goals?
   a) 35 b) 42 c) 50 d) 59

5. Dong Fangzhuo made only one appearance for United. Which country did he come from?
   a) South Korea b) Malaysia c) Thailand d) China

6. Robin Van Persie played 105 games, scoring how many goals?
   a) 36 b) 45 c) 58 d) 65

7. Denis Law made 404 appearances and scored 237 goals. How many hat tricks did he score?
   a) 10 b) 12 c) 15 d) 18

8. Which other player has scored more than 10 hat tricks for United?
   a) Bobby Charlton b) Jack Rowley c) Wayne Rooney
   d) Dennis Viollet

9. Wayne Rooney scored a hat-trick on his Manchester United debut. Which other player scored a hat-trick on his debut for United?
   a) Denis Law b) Eric Cantona c) Charles Sagar d) Andy Cole

10. Who scored a late winner in a 3-2 win against Southampton in the 2017 League Cup final?
    a) Zlatan Ibrahimovic b) Romelu Lukaku c) Alexis Sánchez
    d) Anthony Martial

Answers: Page 127

RUUD VAN NISTELROOY

1. Which club did Manchester United sign Van Nistelrooy from in 2001?
   a) Ajax b) PSV Eindhoven c) Feyenoord d) Napoli

2. At the time it was a British record transfer fee of how much?
   a) £15 million b) £19 million c) £22 million d) £25 million

3. Van Nistelrooy was originally going to sign in the summer of 2000. What stopped the transfer from being completed?
   a) Failing a medical b) Contractual issues c) Suffering a knee injury d) Missing the transfer deadline

4. Which season did he win the PFA Fans' and the PFA Players' Player of the Year award?
   a) 2000/01 b) 2001/02 c) 2002/03 d) 2004/05

5. Van Nistelrooy holds the club record for the most goals in consecutive League games. How many consecutive games did he score in?
   a) 8 b) 10 c) 12 d) 15

6. Ruud scored all four goals in a 4-1 Champs League win against which team in 2003/04?
   a) Lazio b) PSV Eindhoven c) Basel d) Sparta Prague

7. Van Nistelrooy played for five seasons, making 219 appearances. How many goals did he score?
   a) 145 b) 150 c) 160 d) 175

8. During those five seasons, how many times was he the top goalscorer in the Champions League
   a) 1 b) 2 c) 3 d) 4

9. Van Nistelrooy played for the Netherlands 70 times. How many goals did he score?
   a) 30 b) 35 c) 40 d) 45

10. Van Nistelrooy left Manchester United to join which club in 2006?
    a) Real Madrid b) Barcelona c) Juventus d) Ajax

Answers: Page 127

ZLATAN IBRAHIMOVIC

1. Which club did Zlatan join Manchester United from?
   a) Internazionale b) Barcelona c) AC Milan d) PSG

2. Zlatan played for United for just under 2 years. How many trophies did he win in that time?
   a) 1 b) 2 c) 3 d) 4

3. Zlatan has two black belts in which martial art?
   a) Karate b) Taekwondo c) Jiu-Jitsu d) Judo

4. Finish the quote used to explain why he turned down a trial with Arsenal: "Zlatan doesn't do _____"
   a) Auditions b) Losing c) England d) Arsenal

5. In the first week of joining United, how much money did the club make in shirt sales?
   a) £32 million b) £44 million c) £51 million d) £76 million

6. He scored on his Premier League debut against which club?
   a) Derby County b) Bournemouth c) Swansea City d) Everton

7. In his second season with United, he became the first player to represent how many clubs in the Champions League?
   a) 5 b) 6 c) 7 d) 8

8. Zlatan is regarded as one of the greatest strikers of all time and is one of the most decorated, having won how many major trophies?
   a) 25 b) 34 c) 38 d) 41

9. He left Man Utd to join which Major League Soccer team?
   a) DC United b) LA Galaxy c) Orlando City d) New York Red Bulls

10. Which of these clubs has Zlatan not played for?
    a) Milan b) Juventus c) Inter Milan d) Roma

Answers: Page 127

MARK HUGHES

1. **In which Welsh town was Mark Hughes born in 1963?**
   a) Cardiff b) Swansea c) Wrexham d) Newport

2. **What year did Mark Hughes debut for Manchester United?**
   a) 1981 b) 1982 c) 1983 d) 1984

3. **In 1986, Hughes left United to play for which Spanish team for £2 million?**
   a) Atletico Madrid b) Barcelona c) Real Madrid d) Sevilla

4. **He left that club to play for who?**
   a) Ajax b) AC Milan c) Benfica d) Bayern Munich

5. **In 1988, Sir Alex Ferguson re-signed Hughes for how much?**
   a) £500k b) £1 million c) £2 million d) £3 million

6. **How many seasons did he play for Manchester United during this second spell at the club?**
   a) 5 b) 7 c) 9 d) 11

7. **Along with 7 other players, Hughes holds the record for the most yellow cards in a single season. How many is it?**
   a) 11 b) 14 c) 17 d) 20

8. **In total, how many goals did he score for Man Utd?**
   a) 121 b) 163 c) 182 d) 209

9. **Hughes left United for the final time to join which club?**
   a) Blackburn b) Southampton c) Leeds United d) Chelsea

10. **Which team was Hughes' first managerial appointment?**
    a) Blackburn Rovers b) Man City c) FC Basel d) Wales

Answers: Page 127

JACK ROWLEY

1. Rowley shared his nickname with an English club. What was it?
   a) The Saint b) The Hammer c) The Magpie d) The Gunner

2. Manchester United signed Rowley from which club in 1937?
   a) Hartlepools United b) Bournemouth & Boscombe Athletic
   c) Swansea Town d) Clapton Orient

3. He scored twice in the 1948 FA Cup final as Manchester United beat which team 4-2?
   a) Bolton Wanderers b) Blackpool c) Wolverhampton Wanderers
   d) Leicester City

4. Rowley spent 17 years at Manchester United, but the Second World War meant he played 12 seasons. How many goals did he score?
   a) 143 b) 175 c) 194 d) 211

5. How many goals did Rowley score as United won the 1951-52 First Division title?
   a) 27 b) 30 c) 33 d) 36

6. How many seasons did he finish as United's top scorer in all competitions (not including War years)
   a) 3 b) 4 c) 5 d) 6

7. He scored six times for England in how many caps?
   a) 6 b) 12 c) 18 d) 24

8. What relation is he to Arthur Rowley, the top scorer in English league football history, who scored 434 league goals?
   a) Cousin b) Nephew c) Son d) Brother

9. He finished his playing career as player-manager of which club?
   a) New Brighton b) Colchester United c) Scarborough
   d) Plymouth Argyle

10. Rowley spent the 1963-64 season as manager of which European giants?
    a) Ajax b) Benfica c) Roma d) Borussia Dortmund

Answers: Page 127

FUN FACTS, STORIES AND STATS

1. Between the 2002/03 and 2003/04 seasons, Ruud Van Nistelrooy scored in 10 consecutive games, setting the record for scoring in the most consecutive games in the Premier League. Jamie Vardy broke that record in 2015 when he scored in 11 consecutive games for Leichester City during their incredible run to winning the Premier League title.

2. In the 2002-03 season, Ruud Van Nistelrooy scored 12 Champions League goals in 9 consecutive matches. He has scored the most goals in the Champions League for Manchester United with an incredible 35 goals in 43 games.

3. In 1959/60 Dennis Violet set the record for the most goals scored in a single league campaign when he scored 32 times in the old First Division.

4. Having won the Premier League golden boot with Arsenal in 2011/12 with 30 goals. Robin Van Persie won it again during his first season at Manchester United in 2012/13, scoring 26 goals and helping United win their 20th and last league title to date.

5. At times the Bulgarian international Dimitar Berbatov appeared lazy and was often castigated for it by the fans. However, it takes a huge football IQ to make playing at the highest level look like a kickabout in the park. Many would argue that he never quite reached his potential at United, but in the 2010/11 season he helped the club with the Premier League and reach the Champions League Final. He also shared the Golden Boot with Manchester City's Carlos Tevez with 20 goals. He captained the Bulgaria national team bewteem 2006 to 2010, and is the country's all-time leading goalscorer.

6. Local lad Stan Pearson was one of the stars of Matt Busby's first great side. He got four assists on his debut against Chesterfield in 1937. He really began to shine shortly after the Second World War when his goals helped United win the League title in 1952.

7. Teddy Sheringham arrived at Old Trafford from Tottenham Hotspur in 1997 and won three Premier League titles, an FA Cup, and a UEFA Champions League. He will be best remembered for his late equalizer as a substitute against Bayern Munich in the 1999 Champions League final at the Nou Camp. His goal shook the Bayern team and then seconds later he assisted Ole Gunnar Solskjær's winner. It remains one of the most extraordinary substitute appearances in football history.

8. During his short time at Old Trafford Zlatan Ibrahimovic made a huge impact. The charismatic Swedish international joined from PSG in 2016 on a free transfer and helped United win the League Cup and Europa League in his first season. He signed for LA Galaxy in 2018 after scoring 29 goals in 53 appearances for the club. He is Sweden's all-time leading scorer with 62 goals in 116 games.

9. Mark Hughes had two spells at Manchester United. His first was between 1980 and 1986 after signing as a schoolboy aged 14. It was after he returned from two unsuccessful periods at Barcelona and Bayern Munich that he made the most impact at the club. Prone to scoring spectacular goals, he scored 163 goals for the club. Most notably, he scored twice in a 2-1 win against his former club Barcelona in the 1991 European Cup Winners' Cup final. He won two Premier League titles and three FA Cups.

10. Tommy Taylor was another of the Busby Babes whose life was tragically cut short in the Munich air disaster. Taylor was only 26 when he died and could possibly become the club's all-time leading scorer. In his 191 games for United, he scored 131 goals, and for England, he scored 16 goals in 19 games. A tall, strong and imposing player, he was superb in the air.

TRIVIA QUIZ ANSWERS
Chapter 11: Fantastic Forwards - Part 3

STRIKERS - PART 3
1. a) Teddy Sheringham
2. c) 20
3. a) Aston Villa
4. b) 42
5. d) China
6. c) 58
7. d) 18
8. b) Jack Rowley
9. c) Charles Sagar
10. a) Zlatan Ibrahimovic

RUUD VAN NISTELROOY
1. b) PSV Eindhoven
2. b) £19 million
3. c) Suffering a knee injury
4. b) 2001/02
5. b) 10
6. d) Sparta Prague
7. b) 150
8. c) 3
9. b) 35
10. a) Real Madrid

ZLATAN IBRAHIMOVIC
1. d) Paris Saint-Germain
2. c) 3
3. b) Taekwondo
4. a) Auditions
5. d) £76 million
6. b) Bournemouth
7. c) 7
8. b) 34
9. b) LA Galaxy
10. d) Roma

MARK HUGHES
1. c) Wrexham
2. c) 1983
3. b) Barcelona
4. d) Bayern Munich
5. b) £1 million
6. b) 7
7. b) 14
8. b) 163
9. d) Chelsea
10. d) Wales

JACK ROWLEY
1. d) The Gunner
2. b) Bournemouth & Boscombe Athletic
3. b) Blackpool
4. d) 211
5. b) 30
6. c) 5
7. a) 6
8. d) Brother
9. d) Plymouth Argyle
10. a) Ajax

Chapter 12

MANAGERS AND CAPTAINS

MANAGERS

1. Who was the last Englishman to be the club's perminant manager?
   a) Dave Sexton b) Ron Atkinson c) Walter Crickmer
   d) Wilf McGuinness

2. Who is the only man to have managed Man United and Man City?
   a) Sir Matt Busby b) Scott Duncan c) Tommy Docherty
   d) Ernest Mangnall

3. What happened during James West's time, between 1900 and 1903?
   a) The club was founded b) United moved to Old Trafford
   c) The club changed its name d) They won their first trophy

4. Who was caretaker manager of the club in 1958 as Sir Matt Busby recovered in the hospital after the Munich air disaster?
   a) Wilf McGuinness b) Don Revie c) Jimmy Murphy
   d) Kenny Morgans

5. Who took over from Sir Matt Busby when he finally left the club?
   a) Frank O'Farrell b) Lal Hilditch c) Jack Robson d) Dave Sexton

6. Other than Sir Matt Busby, who is the only other manager to have had two spells in charge of United?
   a) Frank O'Farrell b) Herbert Bamlett c) Walter Crickmer
   d) John Bentley

7. Who was the first non-British manager of Manchester United?
   a) Louis van Gaal b) David Moyes c) José Mourinho
   d) Ole Gunnar Solskjaer

8. After Sirs Alex Ferguson and Sir Matt Busby, which manager has taken charge of the most games for the club, with 373?
   a) Ron Atkinson b) Alfred Albut c) Ernest Mangnall d) Dave Sexton

9. How many different Scotsmen have managed Manchester United?
   a) 5 b) 6 7 d) 8

10. In 1926, who was suspended by the FA for "improper conduct in his position as Secretary-Manager of the Manchester United"?
    a) John Chapman b) Herbert Bamblett c) Scott Duncan
    d) Wilf McGuinness

Answers: Page 138

CAPTAINS

1. Which player has served as the club's captain for the longest?
   a) Bryan Robson b) Bobby Charlton c) Martin Buchan
   d) Roy Keane

2. Who was the first non-British captain of the club?
   a) Jack Silcock b) Johnny Carey c) Noel Cantwell d) Eric Cantona

3. Which of the Busby Babes that died in the Munich Air Disaster was club captain at the time?
   a) Billy Whelan b) Roger Byrne c) David Pegg d) Duncan Edwards

4. How many seasons did Steve Bruce spend as United captain?
   a) 1 b) 2 c) 3 d) 4

5. Who was the last man to captain United to relegation?
   a) George Graham b) Martin Buchan c) Maurice Setters
   d) Allenby Chilton

6. Who is currently the only non-European to have been Manchester United captain?
   a) Tim Howard b) Dwight Yorke c) Park Ji-Sung
   d) Antonio Valencia

7. Gary Neville and which other player have been losing club captains in Champions League finals?
   a) Ryan Giggs b) Nemanja Vidic c) Rio Ferdinand d) Wayne Rooney

8. How many trophies did the Manchester United win during Roy Keane's captaincy between 1997 and 2005?
   a) 8 b) 9 c) 10 d) 11

9. Bobby Charlton stood in for whom as captain in the 1968 European Cup final?
   a) George Best b) Pat Crerand c) Denis Law d) Bill Foulkes

10. History repeated itself when, In Keane's absence, who captained Manchester United in the 1999 Champions League final?
    a) Jaap Stam b) David Beckham c) Peter Schmeichel d) David May

Answers: Page 138

SIR MATT BUSBY

1. **Sir Matt Busby was born in Bellshill, ten miles from which city?**
   a) Aberdeen b) Dundee c) Edinburgh d) Glasgow

2. **For which two clubs did Sir Matt Busby play professionally?**
   a) Celtic & Liverpool b) Liverpool & Manchester City
   c) Motherwell & Manchester City d) Celtic & Motherwell

3. **Manchester United won how many trophies during Busby's tenure (including shared Comunity Shields)?**
   a) 7 b) 9 c) 11 d) 13

4. **The first of which was the FA Cup in which year?**
   a) 1948 b) 1950 c) 1951 d) 1953

5. **"Manchester is my heaven" was Busby's response to turning down the chance to manage which team, described by their president as "managing paradise"?**
   a) Benfica b) Roma c) Celtic d) Real Madrid

6. **How long did Busby spend in the hospital recovering from the Munich Air Disaster?**
   a) 3 days b) 10 days c) 4 weeks d) 9 weeks

7. **Busby was manager of Great Britain to what place at the 1948 Olympic football tournament?**
   a) 1st b) 3rd c) 4th d) 8th

8. **In which year did Warrick Road North become Sir Matt Busby Way?**
   a) 1968 b) 1979 c) 1987 d) 1993

9. **In which year did the club unveil a statue of Busby outside Old Trafford?**
   a) 1996 b) 1999 c) 2002 d) 2005

10. **How many years in total was Sir Matt Busby Manchester United's manager?**
    a) 19 b) 21 c) 25 d) 29

Answers: Page 138

SIR ALEX FERGUSON

1. What position did Sir Alex play during his playing career?
a) Goalkeeper b) Defender c) Midfielder d) Striker

2. Which Scottish club did Sir Alex manage before joining United?
a) Falkirk b) Aberdeen c) Rangers d) Celtic

3. In which year was he appointed manager of Manchester United?
a) 1984 b) 1985 c) 1986 d) 1989

4. In what league position did Manchester United finish in Fergie's first season at the club?
a) 7th b) 9th c) 11th d) 13th

5. Fergie won his first trophy with Manchester United in 1990 Which trophy was it?
a) FA cup b) League Cup c) European Cup winners cup
d) The first division

6. Fergie would often scream at his players if they weren't performing. This was dubbed as the "_____" treatment.
a) Tornado b) Hurricane c) Hairdryer d) Rottweiler

7. Sir Alex would ferociouslydo what during matches to help soothe his nervous cough?
a) Smoke cigarettes b) Chew Gum c) Squeeze a tennis ball
d) drink black tea

8. Sir Alex played once for Manchester United during the 1987-88 tour of Bermuda. Against which team did he face?
a) Bermuda Triangles b) Kent Cricket Club c) Island Inlanders
d) Sommerset Cricket Club

9. How many times did Sir Alex take charge of Manchester United?
a) 1100 b) 1300 c) 1500 d) 1700

10. How many trophies did he win during his 27-year reign at the club?
a) 25 b) 31 c) 38 d) 46

Answers: Page 138

FERGIE vs WENGER

1. Man United beat Arsenal 1-0 in the first meeting between Ferguson and Wenger in September 1996. Who scored an own goal that day?
   a) Lee Dixon b) Tony Adams c) Steve Bould d) Nigel Winterburn

2. Complete the quote from Sir Alex on Wenger; "He has no experience of English football. He comes from _____ and now he's telling us how to organise our football."
   a) France b) Nowhere c) University d) Japan

3. The first real clash between the two happened in 1997 after a nasty challenge by Ian Wright on which United player?
   a) Steve Bruce b) Peter Schmeichel c) Dennis Irwin d) Jordi Cruyff

4. Which player was goaded by Arsenal players after missing a last-minute penalty at Old Trafford, only to score in the same fixture in the next season?
   a) Wayne Rooney b) Alan Smith c) Paul Scholes
   d) Ruud van Nistelrooy

5. In October 2004 Manchester United beat Arsenal 2-0 at Old Trafford to end their historic run of 49 games unbeaten. The game will forever be known as what?
   a) Endgame b) Arsgate c) Paingate d) Pizzagate

6. Between 1996 and 2013, how many times did neither Fergie nor Wenger win the Premier League?
   a) 2 b) 3 c) 4 d) 5

7. In what year was Arsene Wenger sent to the stands at Old Trafford?
   a) 2008 b) 2009 c) 2010 d) 2011

8. In their 49 battles, Wenger won 16, how did Fergie win?
   a) 20 b) 23 c) 26 d) 29

9. The two faced off in which year's FA Cup final?
   a) 1999 b) 2004 c) 2005 d) 2007

10. What was the name of the 2018 TV series about their rivalry?
    a) The Touchline b) The Feud c) The Clash
    d) The battle of the buffets

Answers: Page 138

THE POST-FERGIE ERA

1. Since Sir Alex Ferguson's retirement, two of his former players have taken charge as caretaker managers. Can you name them?

2. Who was the first player to score a goal for Manchester United following Sir Alex Ferguson's retirement?
   a) Danny Welbeck b) Ryan Giggs c) Antonio Valencia
   d) Robin van Persie

3. Who was the first Manchester United manager to win a major trophy for the club following Sir Alex Ferguson's retirement?
   a) Louis van Gaal b) David Moyes c) Jose Mourinho
   d) Ole Gunnar Solskjaer

4. Which trophy did they win?
   a) Premier League b) FA Cup c) League Cup d) Europa League

5. In 2014, to whome did former executive vice-chairman Ed Woodward pitch the club as "an adult version of Disneyland."?
   a) Pep Guardiola b) Jose Mourinho c) Carlo Ancelotti
   d) Jurgen Klopp

6. Which United manager said, "I am the manager of one of the greatest clubs in the world but I am also one of the greatest managers in the world"?
   a) Matt Busby b) David Moyes c) Louis van Gaal d) Jose Mourinho

7. Of the first 4 permanent managers, which had the best win rate?
   a) Jose Mourinho b) Louis van Gaal c) Ole Gunnar Solskjaer d) David Moyes

8. Those first four spent a total of eight years in charge, how long had the previous four (including Sir Alex) spent at the helm?
   a) 32 b) 35 c) 37 d) 41

9. After leaving Ralph Rangnick became of manager of which nation?
   a) Austria b) Poland c) Norway d) Switzerland

10. Erik ten Hag became the fifth permanent manager since Fergie left after winning how many trophies as Ajax boss?
    a) 4 b) 5 c) 6 d) 7

Answers: Page 138

FUN FACTS, STORIES AND STATS

1. Sir Matt Busby took charge of the first great era in Manchester United's history. The Scotsman joined the club in 1945. He won his first league title in 1952. He blooded numerous youth talents at the club and his "Busby Babes" won the First Division in 1955-56 and 1956-57. Tragically his team was torn apart in the Munich Air disaster and he too almost lost his life in the crash. In 1968 he lead Manchester United to become the first English club to win the European Cup. He left in 1969 only to return again for the second half of the 1970/71 season. He won 13 major trophies while with the club.

2. Sir Alex Ferguson is the club's longest-serving and most successful manager. Many would argue he is the greatest manager of all time for what he achieved at the club over his 27 year reign. He was in charge of a total of 1,500 games. He won an incredible 13 Premier Leagues, five FA Cups, four League Cups, 10 Community Shields, two Champions Leagues, one UEFA Cup Winners' Cup, one UEFA Super Cup, one Intercontinental Cup and one FIFA Club World Cup.

3. Sir Alex Ferguson was the king of mind games and this often led to feuds with other managers. He once said that Liverpool boss Rafael Benitez's defensive tactics were ruining the game and that Liverpool was unimaginative. He pushed Newcastle United boss Kevin Keagan into his empathised 'I will love it' rant on live TV. But it was his feud with Arsenal manager Arsène Wenger, who he labelled as a novice when he arrived at Arsenal from the Japanese league in 1996, that became the most heated. In the media, Ferguson often belittled Wenger and Wenger refused to shake hands after matches several times. The rivalry exploded in 2004 at Old Trafford when Man United stopped Arsenal's impressive unbeaten streak of 49 games. After the match in the tunnel, Ferguson was hit by a flying pizza as the two sides brawled. The incident was labelled pizzgate by the press. The bitter rivalry between Man Utd and Arsenal in the late 90's and early 00's is yet to be matched in the modern Premier League erah

4. Sir Between 1878 and 1892, the team was selected by a committee. Ernest Mangnall was the first manager to win trophies for the club. He won the 1908 Football League title and the 1909 FA Cup. He left United to join City in 1912.

5. Louis Van Gal was the club's first non-British manager. He joined in May 2014 and in 2016 won the club's first trophy since the departure of Alex Ferguson. He was replaced after 2 years by, Jose Mourinho.

6. José Mourinho won the League Cup, Community Shield, and Europa League in his first season. However, things turned sour in the 2017-18 season after United won only seven of their first 17 games. An unhappy dressing room and queries about his tactics led to him being fired in December 2018. Ole Gunnar Solskjer was then appointed as caretaker-manager.

7. After winning 14 out of 19 games as caretaker manager, in 2019 Ole Gunnar Solskjaer became the first former player to become the club's full-term manager. After poor form, he left the club in 2021. He was the first manager not to win a trophy since Frank 'Farrell.

8. Bryan Robson spent 14 seasons at United. He mane 461 appearances and scored 99 goals. 'Captain Marvel' became the longest-serving captain in the club's history. He made 90 appearances for England and was captain for 65 of them. Only Bobby Moore and Billy Wright have captained England more times than him.

9. Fierce Irishman Roy Keane is the most successful captain in the Premier League era. In total, he won 4 Premier League titles, 2 FA Cups, and a Champions League trophy in his 8 years as club captain. He famously missed the Champions League final in 1999 due to suspension so Peter Schmeichel captained the team on his final appearance for the club.

10. The club have had 50 captains in its history. The first captain of the club was E. Thomas between 1882 and 1883 and the current captain is Harry Maguire. 30 of the captains were British, 11 were Scottish, four were from the Republic of Ireland, two were from Wales, and one each from France, Serbia and Ecuador. Eric Cantona who became the club's first non-British captain in 1996-97.

TRIVIA QUIZ ANSWERS
Chapter 12: Managers and Captains

MANAGERS
1. b) Ron Atkinson
2. d) Ernest Mangnall
3. c) The club changed its name
4. c) Jimmy Murphy
5. a) Frank O'Farrell
6. c) Walter Crickmer
7. a) Louis van Gaal
8. c) Ernest Mangnall
9. b) 6
10. a) John Chapman

CAPTAINS
1. a) Bryan Robson
2. b) Johnny Carey
3. b) Roger Byrne
4. b) 2
5. a) George Graham
6. d) Antonio Valencia
7. b) Nemanja Vidic
8. c) 10
9. c) Denis Law
10. c) Peter Schmeichel

SIR MATT BUSBY
1. d) Glasgow
2. b) Liverpool & Manchester City
3. d) 13
4. a) 1948
5. d) Real Madrid
6. d) 9 weeks
7. c) 4th
8. d) 1993
9. a) 1996
10. c) 25

SIR ALEX FERGUSON
1. d) Striker
2. b) Aberdeen
3. c) 1986
4. c) 11th
5. a) FA cup
6. c) Hairdryer
7. d) Somerset Cricket Club
8. c) 1500
9. c) 38
10.

FERGIE VS WENGER
1. d) Nigel Winterburn
2. d) Japan
3. b) Peter Schmeichel
4. d) Ruud van Nistelrooy
5. d) Pizzagate
6. c) 4
7. b) 2009
8. b) 23
9. c) 2005
10. b) The Feud

THE POST-FERGIE ERA
1. Ryan Giggs & Michael Carrick
2. d) Robin van Persie
3. a) Louis van Gaal
4. b) FA Cup
5. d) Jurgen Klopp
6. d) Jose Mourinho
7. a) Jose Mourinho
8. d) 41
9. a) Austria
10. b) 5

THANK YOU FROM US

We hope that you are enjoying the book and you have learned some facinating trivia about the mighty Red Devils.

Thanks s much for reading it.

Leaving a review so other passionate fans like yourselves can test and expand their knowledge of the club will really help. And it will enable the Beautiful Games team to continue to create the highest quality books possible.

It only takes about 60 seconds and won't cost anything.

Simply scan this QR code:

Thank you so much for your help!

Glory Glory Man United!

Chapter 13
RECORDS AND TROPHIES

ROY
KEANE

DOMESTIC TROPHIES

1. What was the first trophy the club ever won, in 1886?
   a) The Salford cup b) The Manchester Cup
   c) The North West Trophy d) The Northern Shield

2. Which year did Man United win the League Championship for the first time?
   a) 1903 b) 1908 c) 1911 d) 1914

3. In which year did Manchester United win their first FA Cup?
   a) 1909 b) 1911 c) 1912 d) 1915

4. They have won three league and FA Cup doubles, all in the 1990s. In which season did they not win the double?
   a) 1993-94 b) 1995-96 c) 1996-97 d) 1998-99

5. How many times have Manchester United won or shared the Charity/Community Shield?
   a) 21 b) 23 c) 26 d) 28

6. Which of these trophies did United win for the first time in 1992?
   a) Premier League b) League Cup c) Full Members' Cup
   d) Intercontinental Cup

7. Manchester United have won the most league titles. How many have they won?
   a) 17 b) 19 c) 20 d) 22

8. In which season did Manchester United complete the Premier League, FA Cup and European Cup treble?
   a) 1998-99 b) 1999-00 c) 2000-01 d) 2001-02

9. As of 2023 How many times has the club won the FA Cup in its history?
   a) 8 b) 10 c) 12 d) 15

10. As of 2023, how many trophies have Man United won in total?
    a) 39 b) 52 c) 69 d) 75

Answers: Page 149

EUROPEAN TROPHIES

1. **What year did Manchester United win their first-ever European Cup?**
   a) 1966 b) 1967 c) 1968 d) 1969

2. **Which team did they beat in the final at Wembley?**
   a) AC MIlan b) Real Madrid c) Benfica d) PSG

3. **Who scored twice in that final?**
   a) Brian Kidd b) Bobby Charlton c) George Best d) John Aston

4. **How many times have Manchester United played in the final of a European Cup / Champions League?**
   a) 3 b) 4 c) 5 d) 6

5. **How many times have they won the European Cup / Champions League?**
   a) 3 b) 4 c) 5 d) 6

6. **In 1991, United won the European Cup Winners' Cup and which other trophy for the first time?**
   a) Intercontinental Cup b) League Cup c) UEFA Super Cup
   d) Club World Cup

7. **United's win in 1999 was the first triumph by an English club for how many years?**
   a) 6 b) 12 c) 15 d) 17

8. **How many times has United played in the UEFA Super Cup?**
   a) 1 b) 2 c) 3 d) 4

9. **In Manchester United's 2008 Champions League final victory over Chelsea on penalties, who was the only United player to miss a spot-kick?**
   a) Cristiano Ronaldo b) Carlos Tevez c) Paul Scholes d) Alan Smith

10. **Who is Manchester United's highest-ever goal scorer in European competitions with 38 goals?**
    a) Wayne Rooney b) Cristiano Ronaldo c) Ruud van Nistelrooy
    d) Ryan Giggs

Answers: Page 149

MOST APPEARANCES

Using their initials, can you connect the name of the player to the number of appearances they have made for Manchester United?

963   RG

758   BC

718   PS

688   BF

602   GN

559   WR

535   AS

535   TD

529   DI

512   DDG

Answers: Page 149

TOP GOALSCORERS

Using their initials, can you connect the name of the player to
the number of goals they have scored for
Manchester United?

253	WR
249	BC
237	DL
211	JR
179	GB
179	DV
168	RG
168	JS
163	MH
155	PS

Answers: Page 149

CLUB RECORDS

1. Manchester United's record home attendance is 83,260 vs Arsenal in 1948, but where was the match played?
   a) Wembely b) Boundary Park c) Hillsborough d) Maine Road

2. Ryan Giggs holds the record for the most appearances for Man Utd. How many times has he played for the club?
   a) 904 b) 922 c) 963 d) 981

3. Wayne Rooney is the clubs leading scorer with how many goals?
   a) 221 b) 234 c) 253 d) 269

4. United's biggest win was a 10-0 triumph over which team?
   a) Anderlecht b) Partizan Belgrade c) AEK Athens d) Basel

5. What is United's heaviest defeat, which they suffered three times pre-World War Two and once in 2023?
   a) 1-9 b) 0-6 c) 2-9 d) 0-7

6. What is Manchester United's biggest Premier League win?
   a) 8-0 b) 9-0 c) 10-1 d) 11-1

7. Between December 1998 and October 1999, United set their longest ever unbeaten run at how many matches?
   a) 36 b) 40 c) 42 d) 45

8. In which season did the club reach their lowest-ever league position when they finished 20th in the second division and survived relegation by a single point?
   a) 1921-22 b) 1929-30 c) 1933-34 d) 1938-39

9. Between November 2008 and February 2009, United went on their longest league streak without conceding a goal. How many matches was it?
   a) 12 b) 14 c) 16 d) 18

10. Who is the youngest player to have ever played Manchester United, at the age of 16 years and 19 days?
    a) Ryan Giggs b) Duncan Edwards c) Gary Gaskell
    d) Norman Whiteside

Answers: Page 149

FUN FACTS, STORIES AND STATS

1. Ryan Giggs spent 24 seasons at Manchester United and holds the record for the most appearances. He played a total of 963 times for the Red Devils scoring 168 goals. During that time he never once received a red card. He made 64 appearances for Wales and was their manager between 2018 and 2022.

2. Bobby Charlton has made the most appearances in the FA Cup for Man United. He played a total of 78 times. Dennis Law has scored the most FA cup goals for Manchester United with a total of 34.

3. Assistant manager Jimmy Murphy took over while Busby recovered in the hospital. It was left to him to ensure the club carried on after the tragedy. He said at the time: "The Red Devils will rise again. It will be a long, tiring job to rebuild the Red Devils. This time, we'll have to start practically from scratch. But we'll do it. This I do know – United was and, will again, be a great club. We have the greatest club spirit in the world." Two weeks after the crash United played an FA Cup game against Sheffield Wednesday and on a wave of emotion at Old Trafford and despite a patched-up team they won 3-0. They managed to reach the FA Cup final where they played Bolton Wanderers at Wembley. Busby was just about well enough to sit on the bench, however, the match did not go to script and Bolton won the game 2-0.

4. In 1968, ten years after the Munich air disaster, Manchester United became the first English team to win the competition, defeating Benfica in the final 4–1 after extra time at Wembley Stadium in London. Matt Busby, United's manager at the time of the disaster in Munich, survived life-threatening injuries suffered in the crash and was still at the helm for United, and two other Munich survivors played in the game – Bobby Charlton, who scored two goals in the game, and Bill Foulkes.

5. Manchester United has won the most league titles with a total of 20. The closest team to them are Liverpool on 19 and Arsenal on 13. They have won the most Premier league titles with 13.

6. In 2010/11 United set two records in the Champions League. The first was going on the longest run without conceding a goal. They managed to keep a clean sheet for 481 minutes. The second was they became the only team to play six away matches and not concede a goal.

7. Two of the most important and memorable goals in the club's history were scored by substitutes. Teddy Sheringham and Ole Gunnar Solskjar came onto the pitch at Barcelona's Nou Camp with United trailing 1-0 to Bayern Munich in 1999 Champions League final. In 91st minute Sherrigham poked the ball into the net from close range and then 2 minutes later Solskjar scored from a flicked-on header from Sherrigham, making it 2-1. Sir Alex Ferguson summed it up perfectly... "Football, bloody hell"

8. Manchester United have won the FA Cup 12 times. A record only bettered Arsenal's 13. They have appeared in the final 19 times in total. They won the League and FA Cup double in 1993/94, 1995/96 and the treble in 1998/99

9. At 46 years, 281 days, Billy Meredith became the oldest player to ever appear for Manchester United when he played against Derby County in May 1921

10. Outside Old Trafford, there is a statue of George Best, Denis Law and Sir Bobby Charlton. It is called the United Trinity. It's a celebration of first-ever English club team to win the European Cup in 1968.

TRIVIA QUIZ ANSWERS
Chapter 13: Records and Trophies

DOMESTIC TROPHIES
1. b) The Manchester Cup
2. b) 1908
3. a) 1909
4. c) 1996–97
5. a) 21
6. b) League Cup
7. c) 20
8. a) 1998–99
9. c) 12
10. c) 69

EUROPEAN TROPHIES
1. c) 1968
2. c) Benfica
3. b) Bobby Charlton
4. c) 5
5. a) 3
6. c) UEFA Super Cup
7. c) 15   d) 17
8. d) 4
9. a) Cristiano Ronaldo
10. c) Ruud van Nistelrooy

MOST APPEARANCES
963. Ryan Giggs
758. Bobby Charlton
718. Paul Scholes
688. Bill Foulkes
602. Gary Neville
559. Wayne Rooney
535. Alex Stepney
535. Tony Dunne
529. Denis Irwin
511. David De Gea

TOP GOALSCORERS
253. Wayne Rooney
249. Bobby Charlton
237. Denic Law
211. Jack Rowley
179. George Best
179. Dennis Viollet
168. Ryan Giggs
168. Joe Spence
163. Mark Hughes
155. Paul Scholes

CLUB RECORDS
1. d) Maine Road
2. c) 963
3. c) 253
4. a) Anderlecht
5. d) 0–7
6. b) 9–0
7. d) 45
8. c) 1933/34
9. b) 14
10. c) Gary Gaskell

Chapter 14
PLAYERS AND TRANSFERS

ZLATAN
IBRAHIMOVIĆ

SQUAD NUMBERS

1. What shirt number does the club's mascot "Fred the red" wear?
   a) 17 b) 25 c) 55 d) 99

2. What was the squad number of Manchester United's captain, Bobby Charlton, during the 1968 European Cup final?
   a) 7 b) 8 c) 9 d) 10

3. Who was United's number 15 for the 1998-99 treble season?
   a) Jesper Blomkqvist b) Karel Poborsky c) Ronny Johnson
   d) Jordie Cruyff

4. Which number did Paul Pogba wear during his first spell at Manchester United?
   a) 21 b) 29 c) 38 d) 42

5. Which number did Marcus Rashford wear before taking the number 10 shirt?
   a) 18 b) 19 c) 22 d) 26

6. Eric Cantona was given 7 as his squad number in 1993 with Bryan Robson given 12, but in that season's Champions League Robson wore 7 when he played, meaning Canton wore which number?
   a) 8 b) 9 c) 10 d) 11

7. Which of these numbers did Ryan Giggs not wear for Manchester United in the 1991-92 season?
   a) 2 b) 3 c) 4 d) 5

8. Which Manchester United squad number links Henrikh Mkhitaryan, Nick Powell and Fabio?
   a) 15 b) 22 c) 26 d) 30

9. Which of these Manchester United players did not move from a 1-11 number to a higher one?
   a) Luke Shaw b) Antonio Valencia c) Marcos Rojo
   d) Owen Hargreaves

10. Which of these United players wore number 92 at a previous club?
    a) Victor Lindelöf b) Diogo Dalot c) Raphaël Varane d) Fred

Answers: Page 163

TRANSFERS

1. **Who was Sir Alex Ferguson's first signing for Manchester United**
   a) Viv Anderson   b) Steve Bruce   c) Bryan McClair   d) Mark Hughes

2. **Who was Sir Alex Ferguson's most expensive signing?**
   a) Wayne Rooney   b) Dimitar Berbatov   c) Juan Sebastian Veron
   d) Robin Van Persie

3. **As of 2023 who is Manchester United's most expensive signing?**
   a) Paul Pogba   b) Jadon Sancho   c) Bruno Fernandes
   d) Harry Maguire

4. **What was the transfer fee?**
   a) £79 million   b) £89 million   c) £93 million   d) £102 million

5. **Manchester United's most expensive transfer sale was for who?**
   a) Angel Di Maria   b) Paul Pogba   c) Cristiano Ronaldo
   d) Romelu Lukaku

6. **What was the transfer fee?**
   a) £70 million   b) £80 million   c) £90 million   d) £100 million

7. **How much did Real Madrid pay for David Beckham in 2003?**
   a) £21 million   b) £24.5 million   c) £28.5 million   d) £32 million

8. **Who did Sir Alex Ferguson sign for £305k? and describe as "the bargain of the century"**
   a) Paul Ince   b) Dwight Yorke   c) Andy Cole   d) Peter Schmeichel

9. **In the 1995/96 season Manchester United signed three players over the course of the season, what was unusual about the trio?**
   a) None of them made an appearance   b) They were all goalkeepers
   c) They all scored on debut   d) They were all called Tony

10. **Which of these players is not in the list of United's top 10 most expensive signings as of 2023?**
    a) Antony   b) Jadon Sancho   c) Aaron Wan-Bissaka
    d) Alexis Sanchez

Answers: Page 163

FIND THE PLAYERS

Can you find the 25 players who have made at least one appearance for Manchester United?

1. Oleg Salenko
2. Gerard Piqué
3. Juninho Paulista
4. Paul Pogba
5. Giuseppe Rossi
6. Steve Archibald
7. Henrik Larsson
8. Geremi
9. Lee Chapman
10. Peter Beardsley
11. John Sivebæk
12. Davor Šuker
13. Klaas-Jan Huntelaar
14. Michael Owen
15. Li Tie
16. Karel Poborský
17. Jordi Cruyff
18. Neil Shipperley
19. Juan Sebastián Verón
20. Ryan Shawcross
21. Marco Materazzi
22. Frank de Boer
23. Gabriel Heinze
24. Maicon
25. Nick Barmby
26. John Curtis
27. Clive Allen
28. Stephen Hughes
29. Dion Dublin
30. Ronnie Wallwork
31. Savo Milošević
32. Rui Costa
33. Andy Goram
34. Michael Keane
35. Darren Anderton
36. David Bellion
37. Luke Chadwick
38. Mark Robins
39. Gilles Grimandi
40. Ronald Koeman
41. Massimo Taibi
42. George Graham
43. Lothar Matthäus
44. Gary Walsh
45. William Prunier
46. Nicky Barnby
47. Trevor Sinclair
48. Laurent Blanc
49. Anders Limpar
50. Papa Bouba Diop

Answers: Page 162

COUNTRYMEN

Can you connect the Manchester United player to the country they are they from?

1. Anders Lindegaard
2. Juan Mata
3. Odion Ighalo
4. Carlos Tevez
5. Casemiro
6. Dimitar Berbatov
7. Mark Bosnich
8. Raphaël Varane
9. Jesper Blomqvist
10. Marouane Fellaini
11. Diego Forlán
12. Ji-sung Park
13. Karel Poborsky
14. Alexis Sánchez
15. Eric Bailly
16. Tim Howard
17. Matteo Darmian
18. Nani
19. Henning Berg
20. Daley Blind

a. Australia
b. Belgium
c. Spain
d. Ivory Coast
e. Norway
f. Denmark
g. Sweden
h. Chile
i. Portugal
j. Nigeria
k. Bulgaria
l. USA
m. Italy
n. France
o. Brazil
p. Argentina
q. Uruguay
r. South Korea
s. Czech Republic
t. Netherlands

Answers: Page 162

PLAYERS CHANTS

Which Manchester United players
are these chants about?

1. **Ooh Aah, Ooh Aah, Ooh Aah**
   <_____>
   a) Cantona b) Martial c) Pallister d) Roy Keane

2. <_____ _____>
   He came from Uruguay
   He made the Scousers cry
   a) Edinson Cavani b) Diego Forlan c) Facundo Pellistri
   d) Guillermo Varela

3. <_____>
   <_____ > **will tear you apart (again)**
   a) Giggs b) Scholes c) Cole d) Nani

4. **You are my** < _____>
   My < _____>
   You make me happy
   When skies are grey
   a) Ole Solskjaer b) Cristiano Ronaldo c) Teddy Sheringham
   d) Dwight Yorke

5. **Twenty times, twenty times, Man United**
   Twenty times, twenty times, I say
   Twenty times, twenty times, Man United
   Playing football the <_____> <_____> **way**
   a) Alex Ferguson way b) Roy Keane c) Matt Busby d) Ten Hag

6. It's <_____> you know
   It's hard to believe it's not Scholes
   It's < _____> you know
   a) Giggs b) Butt c) Beckham d) Carrick

7. <_____> <_____> came from France
   The English press said he had no chance
   Fifty million down the drain
   <_____> <_____> scores again
   a) Tony Martial b) Paul Pogba c) Louis Saha d) Eric Cantona

8. Viva <_____> Viva <_____>
   Running Down The Wing
   Hear United Sing
   Viva <_____>
   a) Ronaldo b) Nani c) Kanchelskis d) Giggs

9. <_____> <_____> is a Red,
   Is a Red, Is a Red,
   <_____> <_____> is a Red,
   He hates Scousers!
   a) Phil Neville b) Gary Neville c) Paul Scholes d) David Beckham

10. From Wythenshawe and loves to fight
    He's born to play in red and white
    So listen close, it must be said
    Like Manchester, <_____> is red
    a) Marcus Rashford b) Paul Scholes c) Wes Brown d) Nicky Butt

Answers: Page 163

WHO AM I?

Can you name the Manchester United legend
based on the description of who they are?

1. I was born in Argentina in 1988. At the age of 4, I was transferred from my local club for 35 footballs. Since then I have played for some of the biggest clubs in Europe, including Benfica, Real Madrid, PSG & Juventus. I am a world cup winner.

2. I have had 169 million euros spent on me in transfer fees. I have played for six European clubs who have all won the European cup / Champions League, but I have personally never won it. I was born in 1981. I have played in 3 European championships and one world and I am the top goalscorer for my country.

3. Born in 1940, I started my professional playing career for Huddersfield town. As well as playing for Manchester United, I have also played twice for bitter rivals Manchester City. I played 27 games for the Italian club Torino. I made one appearance at the 1974 world cup against Zaire.

4. As well as playing for Manchester United I have also played in the National Premier Leagues Queensland, Hong Kong First Division, North American Soccer League, League of Ireland and the Scottish first division. I was born in 1946 and I played for my country 37 times, but never at a world cup.

5. I was born in the northeast of England but began my career at Gillingham. I was once joint-top scorer in a league campaign for Manchester United despite being a defender. Between 1998 and 2022, I managed 12 different clubs. I am considered one of the best English footballers to never win an international cap.

6. I was born in Belfast and discovered by the same scout who found George Best. I won the FA Cup twice, scoring an extra time winner in the final against Everton, the only other club I played for. I am still the youngest player to play at the World Cup.

7. I spent five years at Manchester United during the 1980s, after playing for two clubs in my native Scotland. I scored a goal at the 1986 World Cup and went on to manage my country, as well as Celtic and Coventry City. I played for Sir Alex Ferguson's successful Aberdeen team before joining United.

8. I was born in Warrington in the early 1990s and joined the Manchester United academy in 2000. In 2018 I launched my own clothing brand and scored for England at the World Cup. I'm well known for my goal celebrations. I scored an FA Cup final winning goal for Man United.

9. My Manchester United career spanned 12 years, all under Sir Alex Ferguson. I won the Champions League but I was not a treble winner. I am a centurion for my national team. I am a defender who went on to play for Sunderland.

10. I began my youth career with Real Oviedo. I won the Champions League with another English club, then won three trophies as a United player. I launched the charitable movement Common Goal in 2018. I won the 2010 World Cup and I scored in the 2012 European Championship final.

Answers: Page 163

PLAYER NICKNAMES

Can you match the Manchester United players to their nicknames?

1. George Graham
2. David de Gea
3. Nemanja Matić
4. Marcus Rashford
5. Peter Schmeichel
6. Ole Gunnar Solskjaer
7. Mark Hughes
8. Gary Pallister
9. Javier Hernández
10. Paul Pogba

a. The great Dane
b. Dolly
c. The Kid
d. Stroller
e. Monster
f. Sparkey
g. Chicharito 'the little pea'
h. Sticky Gloves
i. La Pioche
j. The baby faced assassin

Answers: Page 163

FUN FACTS, STORIES AND STATS

1. Former United player Lou Macari owns the 'Lou Macari Fish and Chip Shop' near Old Trafford. It is a regular stop-off for fans on matchdays and is usually packed before and after home matches.

2. Billy Meredith was the first footballing superstar. He helped the club with its first five trophies. The 1908 and 1911 Division One titles, the 1909 FA Cup and the 1908 and 1911 Charity Shields. This, after having captained Manchester City to their first-ever trophy, the 1904 FA Cup. The 'Welsh Wizard' used to chew a toothpick during games to help him concentrate.

3. It is reported that during his first week at Manchester United, the sales of Zlatan Ibrahimovic's number nine Manchester United shirt brought in a massive £76 million in revenue. The shirt sales alone will more than cover his £200k weekly salary.

4. Cristiano Ronaldo is the only player to win the European Golden Boot while playing for Manchester United? He earnt this when he scored 31 goals in 2009.

5. Sir Alex Ferguson's first club signing was Viv Anderson. He bought him for £250,000 from Arsenal in 1987.

6. Sir Alex Ferguson made 105 signings during his time at Manchester United. He has stated that his best bargain was singing Peter Schmeichel from Brondby for £500,000 in 1991

7. Cristiano Ronaldo's left United for Real Madrid in 2009, for a world-record transfer fee of £80 million. He had already won a Ballon d'Or at United and went on to win four more during his time at the Santiago Bernabeu. He also won four Champions Leagues and he became Real's highest-ever goalscorer with an extraordinary 451 goals in 438 appearances. His rivalry in Spain with Lionel Messi will go down as one of the greatest in football history.

8. During the 1991 European Cup winner's cup success, United played Wrexham FC. They went on to win the tie 5-0 on aggregate. Wrexham-born Mark Hughes played in the home leg at Old Trafford

9. Paul Pogba became the record signing for Manchester United when he was signed from Juventus for £94.5million in 2016. He had previously left the club in 2012. Pogba's inconsistency frustrated fans and he failed to live up to his huge price tag. He left the club on a free transfer in 2022 and returned back to Juventus.

10. After singing in the summer of 2016, It took Paul Pogba until the end of September to score his first goal for the club. When he did, he whipped out his signature dab dance while dancing with team-mate Jesse Lingard. The dance involves bending one arm towards yourself with your other arm pointing away towards the sky and then dipping your head into the crook of your elbow.

COUNTRYMEN

1. Anders Lindegaard
2. Juan Mata
3. Odion Ighalo
4. Carlos Tevez
5. Casemiro
6. Dimitar Berbatov
7. Mark Bosnich
8. Raphaël Varane
9. Jesper Blomqvist
10. Marouane Fellaini
11. Diego Forlán
12. Ji-sung Park
13. Karel Poborsky
14. Alexis Sánchez
15. Eric Bailly
16. Tim Howard
17. Matteo Darmian
18. Nani
19. Henning Berg
20. Daley Blind

f) Denmark
c) Spain
j) Nigeria
p) Argentina
o) Brazil
k) Bulgaria
a) Australia
n) France
g) Sweden
b) Belgium
q) Uruguay
r) South Korea
s) Czech Republic
h) Chile
d) Ivory Coast
l) USA
m) Italy
i) Portugal
e) Norway
t) Netherlands

FIND THE PLAYER

2. Gerard Piqué
4. Paul Pogba
5. Giuseppe Rossi
7. Henrik Larsson
10. Peter Beardsley
11. John Sivebæk
14. Michael Owen
16. Karel Poborský
17. Jordi Cruyff
19. Juan Sebastián Verón
20. Ryan Shawcross
23. Gabriel Heinze
26. John Curtis
29. Dion Dublin
30. Ronnie Wallwork
33. Andy Goram
34. Michael Keane
36. David Bellion
37. Luke Chadwick
38. Mark Robins
41. Massimo Taibi
42. George Graham
44. Gary Walsh
45. William Prunier
48. Laurent Blanc

TRIVIA QUIZ ANSWERS
Chapter 14: Players and Transfers

SQUAD NUMBERS
1. c) 55
2. c) 9
3. a) Jesper Blomkqvist
4. d) 42
5. b) 19
6. b) 9
7. b) 3
8. b) 22
9. d) Owen Hargreaves
10. a) Victor Lindelöf

TRANSFERS
1. a) Viv Anderson
2. b) Dimitar Berbatov
3. a) Paul Pogba
4. b) £89 million
5. c) Cristiano Ronaldo
6. b) £80 million
7. b) £24.5 million
8. d) Peter Schmeichel
9. b) They were all goalkeepers
10. d) Alexis Sanchez

PLAYER CHANTS
1. a) Eric Cantona
2. b) Diego Forlan
3. a) Ryan Giggs
4. a) Ole Solskjaer
5. c) Matt Busby
6. d) Michael Carrick
7. a) Tony Martial
8. a) Ronaldo
9. b) Gary Neville
10. a) Marcus Rashford

WHO AM I
1. Ángel Di María
2. Zlatan Ibrahimovic
3. Denis Law
4. George Best
5. Steve Bruce
6. Norman Whiteside
7. Gordon Strachan
8. Jesse Lingard
9. John O'Shea
10. Juan Mata

PLAYER NICKNAMES
1. d) Stroller
2. h) Sticky Gloves
3. e) Monster
4. c) The Kid
5. a) The great Dane
6. j) The baby faced - assassin
7. f) Sparkey
8. b) Dolly
9. g) Chicharito - 'the little pea'
10. i) La Pioche

Chapter 15
THE RANDOM ROUND

TRUE OR FALSE

1. As of 2021, Manchester United players have won more PFA Player of the Year and Young Player of the Year awards than any other club

2. Legendary managers Sir Matt Busby and Sir Alex Ferguson were both born and raised in the Govan area of Glasgow

3. As of 2023, Manchester United have included an academy graduate in every matchday squad since 1937, a run of more than 4,000 consecutive games

4. As of 2023, Manchester United players have won more PFA Player of the Year and Young Player of the Year awards than any other club

5. Legendary managers Sir Matt Busby and Sir Alex Ferguson were both born and raised in the Govan area of Glasgow

6. When Ole Gunnar Solskjær was appointed in 2018 he became the first former Manchester United player to be named manager on a permanent basis since Wilf McGuinness in 1969

7. The club's nickname, the Red Devils, was taken from the nearby Salford rugby league team

8. To celebrate Bryan McClair's winning goal in the 1994 FA Cup final, Greggs named his favourite desert, the chocolate Eclair, after him. They called it the Bryan Eclair

9. Old Trafford was badly damaged by bomb during air raids during World War Two

10. The 1974-75 season is United's only season outside the top flight to date

Answers: Page 174

MISCELLANEOUS

1. **Which year did the club add the image of a Red Devil to the badge?**
a) 1969 b) 1973 c) 1978 d) 1982

2. **In 1982 Pope John Paul II visited Manchester but refused to meet with any Manchester United players or staff for what reason?**
a) Only two players were Catholic b) An illness at the club
c) It's unfair to bless only one team d) The devil on the club's badge

3. **What year was Manchester United Womens Football Club formed?**
a) 2016 b) 2017 c) 2018 d) 2019

4. **After playing 20 games between 1972 and 1975, which former player went on to play county cricket for Yorkshire and England?**
a) James Kelly b) Arnold Sidebottom c) Gordon Hill d) Joe Jordan

5. **Which commentator uttered, "Can Manchester United score? They always score", moments before Teddy Sheringham's equaliser in the Champions League final?**
a) Jon Champion b) Brian Moore c) Clive Tyldesley d) John Motson

6. **Plans to do what sparked protests from fans in 2020?**
a) Build a new stadium b) Join the European Super League
c) Unveil a statue of the Glazers d) Change the name of the stadium

7. **Manchester United reached number 1 in the UK Singles Chart with "Come on You Reds" which was produced by which band?**
Oasis b) Fleetwood Mac c) Status Quo d) Manic Street preachers

8. **Australia have won three World Cups at Old Trafford in which sport?**
a) Cricket b) Rugby league c) Hockey d) Ruby 7s

9. **The club was saved in 1901 after a series of events starting with what?**
a) A newspaper advertisement b) A cancelled train to Birmingham
c) A St Bernard dog walking into a pub d) A drunk coal minor

10. **BBC Songs of Praise was recorded at Old Trafford in which year?**
a) 1992 b) 1993 c) 1994 c) 1999

Answers: Page 174

ANOGRAMS

Can you find the name of the manchester United players that are hidden inside these anagrams?

Unscramble the letters to reveal their names

1. EYE ON NORWAY
2. KOREA YEN
3. BREW SNOW
4. INROAD FINDER
5. RADICAL ONION SORT
6. CANINE ACTOR
7. GO GET BEES
8. LADY CONE
9. HES A LAD IN KNICKERS
10. IN EVERY GALL

Answers: Page 174

CLUB MASCOTS

Can you match the Manchester United mascots to the year they were part of the club?

1. 1890s
2. 1902–1906
3. 1906–1909
4. 1930s – 1940s
5. 1940s – 1963
6. 1990 onwards

a. Major the Saint Bernard dog
b. "Hoppy" Thorne, the wne-legged wonder
c. Billy the Goat
d. Michael the Bank Street Canary
e. Fred the Red
f. Jack Irons

Answers: Page 174

FAMOUS QUOTES

1. "It's a special club. It's got history. When I slip on the Manchester United shirt, it's like I'm wearing its past. So you have to sacrifice yourself for this club."
   a) Patrice Evra b) Harry Maguire c) Paul Ince d) Zlatan Ibrahimovic

2. "Winning the Ballon d'Or never bothered me. I just wanted to play for Manchester United."
   a) David Beckham b) Paul Scholes c) Wayne Rooney
   d) Ruud Van Nistelrooy

3. "I was forever in search of a club like Manchester United. United is great and difficult at the same time. Great because we always the chance of winning something. Difficult on that account, because we always have to win."
   a) Cristiano Ronaldo b) Eric Cantona c) Paul Pogba d) Erik ten Hag

4. "At Manchester we strive for perfection and if we fail we might just have to settle for excellence"
   a) Roy Keane b) Sir Alex Ferguson c) Jose Mourinho
   d) Sir Matt Busby

5. "I am a lover of football. Manchester United breathe football. I always listen to the little boy inside of me in these situations - when you have to make the harder decisions in life. What does he want? That boy was screaming for Man United."
   a) Wayne Rooney b) Robin Van Persie c) Ruud Van Nistelrooy
   d) Paul Pogba

6. "I feel close to the rebelliousness and vigour of the youth here. Perhaps time will separate us, but nobody can deny that here, behind the windows of Manchester, there is an insane love of football, of celebration and of music."
   a) Zlatan Ibrahimovic b) Eric Cantona c) Roy Keane d) Paul Pogba

7. **"Manchester is my heaven"**
   a) Matt Busby b) Bobby Charlton b) Eric Cantona
   d) Sir Alex Ferguson

8. **"I never comment on referees and I'm not going to break the habit of a lifetime for that prat."**
   a) Alex Ferguson b) Ron Atkinson c) Matt Busby d) Jose Mourinho

9. **"When you play for United, you have to prove that you are a good player. Manchester United is an institution. Every one of us is very happy that we have the chance to play at Old Trafford, that is a privilege, I know that"**
   a) Rio Ferdinand b) Bryan Robson c) Nemanja Vidić
   d) Mark Hughes

10. **"George Best inspired me when I was young. He was flamboyant and exciting and able to inspire his teammates. I actually think we were very similar players – dribblers who were able to create moments of magic."**
    a) Cristiano Ronaldo b) Pele c) Diago Maradona d) Leo Messi

Answers: Page 174

FUN FACTS, STORIES AND STATS

1. In September 2003, Rio Ferdinand failed to attend a drug test at United's Carrington training ground after he had left to go shopping. When he remembered and returned, it was too late. The FA imposed an eight-month ban from January 2004 at both club and international level meaning he missed the rest of the season and some of the next, as well as all of Euro 2004.

2. Eric Cantona began his acting career during his suspension from football in 1995 His first role was as a rugby player in the French film Happiness is in the Field. Since stepping into acting Cantona has amassed over 30 credits and continues to perform. His most notable roles came in the BAFTA award-winning Elizabeth in 1998 where he starred alongside Cate Blanchett, and Looking for Eric, a 2009 film directed by Ken Loach.

3. The club won its first FA Cup in 1909. They beat Bristol City 1-0 at Crystal Palace, London. The Scot Sandy Turnbull scored the winner and Ernest Mangnall was the manager.

4. During the 1890s, readers of Newton Heath F.C. match programmes would have seen advertisements to hear "Michael the Bank Street Canary sing" for a small fee. However, Michael was not a canary. He was actually a goose, that couldn't sing. It was a money-making scheme used by the club during its financial difficulties. Michael mysteriously disappeared one Christmas and legend has it that a disgruntled fan cooked it for his Christmas dinner.

5. Manchester United won the Premier League for three years in a row between 1998-99 and 2000-01 and between 2006/07 and 2008-09. The only other teams to have done this are Liverpool between 1981-82 and 1983-84. Huddersfield Town between 1923-24 and 1925-26. Arsenal between 1932-33 and 1934-35.

6. In the early 1900's with the club in financial difficulty, club captain Harry Stafford would send Major, his prized Saint Bernard dog, around the crowd with a collection box on its collar to try and bring in much-needed extra funds. In 1901 the dog went missing and was eventually found in possession of local brewer John Henry Davies, who wanted to keep the dog as a pet for his daughter. Stafford convinced Davies to invest £500 in Newton Heath F.C. to help guarantee the club's financial security. In return, he gave Davies the dog. Davies was appointed chairman, and in 1902 he renamed the club Manchester United F.C. and changed the club's colours to red and white.

7. After Major retired, the club needed a new mascot. Half-back Charlie Roberts, who had recently been given a goat by a local theatre company which he had named the Billy. Billy the Goat became the club's third mascot. Billy was paraded around the ground before home matches. He used to travel with the team to ale houses and would often share a drink with them. After the FA Cup Final win in 1909, Billy drank too much champagne and died of alcohol poisoning shortly after. His head is preserved in the Manchester United Museum.

8. William "Hoppy" Thorne was a British soldier who lost a leg during the First World War. He managed to get a job at Old Trafford, cleaning up after home matches and operating the scoreboard at reserve matches. He became famous to the fans because, before home matches, he would take off his clothes, jump over the fence and hop around the pitch.

9. John Thomas "Jack" Irons was the Manchester United mascot from the end of the second World War to the mid-sixties. Before kick-off, he used to stroll around the pitch in a red-and-white dinner suit holding a red-and-white umbrella while signing autographs for fans.

10. Since the early 1990s, Fred the Red has been the Manchester United mascot. The "Red Devil" appears in full kit with the number 55 on the back of his shirt. He entertains the crowd before matches and his likeness is used in the club's merchandising, especially things that are targeted towards children.

TRIVIA QUIZ ANSWERS
Chapter 15: The Random Round

TRUE OR FALSE
1. True
2. True
3. True
4. True
5. False
6. True
7. True
8. False
9. True
10. False

MISCELLANEOUS
1. b) 1973
2. d) The devil on the badge
3. c) 2018
4. b) Arnold Sidebottom
5. c) Clive Tyldesley
6. b) Join the European Super League
7. c) Status Quo
8. b) Rugby league
9. c) A St Bernard dog walking into a pub
10. c) 1994

ANOGRAMS
1. Wayne Rooney
2. Roy Keane
3. Wes Brown
4. Rio Ferdinand
5. Cristiano Ronaldo
6. Eric Cantona
7. George best
8. Andy cole
9. Andrei Kanchelskis
10. Gary Neville

CLUB MASCOTS
1. 1890s
   d) Michael the Bank Street Canary
2. 1902–1906
   a) Major the Saint Bernard dog
3. 1906–1909
   c) Billy the Goat
4. 1930s – 1940s
   b) "Hoppy" Thorne, the
5. 1940s – 1963
   f) Jack Irons
6. 1990 onwards
   e) Fred the Red

FAMOUS QUOTES
1. a) Patrice Evra
2. b) Paul Scholes
3. b) Eric Cantona
4. d) Sir Matt Busby
5. b) Robin Van Persie
6. b) Eric Cantona
7. a) Matt Busby
8. b) Ron Atkinson
9. c) Nemanja Vidić
10. c) Diago Maradona

Chapter 16
FANMOUS STARTING LINEUPS

OLE
GUNNAR
SOLSKJAER

1968
EUROPEAN CUP FINAL
MAN UTD vs BENFICA

Can you name the starting line up?

Answers: Page 185

1994
FA CUP FINAL
MAN UTD vs CHELSEA

Can you name the starting line up?

Answers: Page 185

1999
CHAMPIONS LEAGUE FINAL
MAN UTD vs BAYERN MUNICH

Can you name the starting line up?

Answers: Page 185

2008
CHAMPIONS LEAGUE FINAL
MAN UTD vs CHELSEA

Can you name the starting line up?

Answers: Page 185

2023
LEAGUE CUP FINAL
MAN UTD vs NEWCASTLE UNITED

Can you name the starting line up?

Answers: Page 185

FUN FACTS, STORIES AND STATS

1. On 29th May 1968, in front of a crowd of 92,225 at England's Wembley Stadium, Manchester United became the first English side to win the European Cup. Beating Portugal's Benfica 4-1 after extra time. The game was 1-1 at the end of normal time. In the third minute of extra time, George Best dribbled the ball past the Benfica defence, and goalkeeper and slotted the ball into an empty net. Two minutes later Bryan Kidd scored United's second. In the ninth minute, Charlton scored his second to make the final score 4-1.

2. Manager Sir Matt Busby was knighted for his achievement in rebuilding the club into European champions after the devastation of the Munich Air Disaster. He said "When Bobby [Charlton] took the cup, it cleansed me. It eased the pain of the guilt of going into Europe. It was my justification. This is the most wonderful thing that has happened in my life."

3. On a soaking wet afternoon at Wembley Stadium on 14th May 1994, Manchester thrashed Chelsea 4-0 in the FA Cup final to win the club's first domestic double. Weeks earlier United had won the Premier League however in the first half Chelsea looked the better team. However two penalties from Eric Cantona and a goal each from Mark Hughes and Bryan McClair sealed it for United.

4. Having both been drawn in Group D, Man Utd and Bayern Munich had already played each other twice before the final of the 1999 Champions League. Both games ended in a 2-2 and 1-1 draw. Bayern won the group while United qualified for the knockout phase as one of the two best runners-up across all six groups.

5. United went into the 1999 final without first-choice midfielder Paul Scholes and club captain Roy Keane. Both had received a second yellow card in the competition in the previous match against Juventus. Ferguson brought in Blomqvist and Butt to replace Scholes and Keane, moved Beckham from right-wing to centre-midfield and moved Giggs from the left to the right wing. This was Peter Schmeichel's last game for the club and he captained the team.

6. Bayern Munich's Mario Basler scored a free kick after six minutes. Bayern then had numerous opportunities to extend their lead. They hit the post and crossbar and Peter Schmeichel had to make numerous saves. Ferguson brought on Solskjær and Sheringham and with almost the last attack of the game, Beckham swung a corner into the box. The ball was partially cleared before Giggs sent a low volley into the path of Sheringham, whose scuffed shot squeezed found the back of the net. Almost immediately United won another corner. Beckham again whipped it in and it Sheringham nodded it to Solskjær who toe-poked it into the roof of the net, completing one of the most outrageous and dramatic comebacks in football history.

7. Only ten teams have managed to go through the entire European Cup / Champions League without losing a match. United did this in the 1998-99 tournament managing 5 wins and 6 draws. They played Bayern Munich, Brondby and Barcelona in the group stages and Inter Milan and Juventus in the knockout stages

8. On May 21st, 2008 at the Luzhniki Stadium in Moscow in Russia, Manchester United beat Chelsea 6-5 on penalties to win their third, and Alex Ferguson's second, European crown. Coincidently it marked the 100th anniversary of the club's first league triumph, the 50th anniversary of the Munich air disaster, and the 40th anniversary of their first European Cup triumph.

9. Ronaldo scored United's opening goal before Chelsea's Frank Lampard equalised before halftime. The game ended 1-1 and towards the end of extra time, Chelsea's Didier Drogba was sent off for slapping Nemanja Vidić. Ronaldo missed United's third penalty kick, giving John Terry the chance to win the cup for Chelsea. However, the Chelsea captain slipped and his shot hit the post. Edwin van der Sar then saved Nicolas Anelka's penalty to secure a Premier League and Champions League double.

10. The club also went unbeaten during the 2007-08 champions League campaign, they won five of their six group matches against Sporting Lisbon, Dynamo Kyiv and Roma. then in the knockout stages, they made their way past Lyon, Roma and Barcelona. They ended with nine wins and four draws.

TRIVIA QUIZ ANSWERS

Chapter 16: Famous Starting Lineups

BENFICA - 1968

1. Alex Stepney
2. Shay Brennan
3. Tony Dunne
4. Pat Crerand
5. Bill Foulkes
6. Nobby Stiles
7. George Best
8. Brian Kidd
9. Bobby Charlton (c)
10. David Sadler
11. John Aston

CHELSEA - 1994

1. Peter Schmeichel
2. Paul Parker
3. Steve Bruce (c)
4. Gary Pallister
5. Denis Irwin
6. Andrei Kanchelskis
7. Paul Ince
8. Roy Keane
9. Ryan Giggs
10. Mark Hughes
11. Eric Cantona

BAYERN MUNICH - 1999

1. Peter Schmeichel (c)
2. Gary Neville
3. Ronny Johnsen
4. Jaap Stam
5. Denis Irwin
6. Ryan Giggs
7. David Beckham
8. Nicky Butt
9. Jesper Blomqvist
10. Dwight Yorke
11. Andy Cole

CHELSEA - 2008

1. Edwin van der Sar
2. Wes Brown
3. Rio Ferdinand (c)
4. Serbia Nemanja Vidić
5. Patrice Evra
6. Owen Hargreaves
7. Paul Scholes
8. Michael Carrick
9. Cristiano Ronaldo
10. Wayne Rooney
11. Carlos Tevez

NEWCASTLE UNITED - 2023

1. David De Gea
20. Diogo Dalot
19. Raphaël Varane
6. Lisandro Martínez
23. Luke Shaw
18. Casemiro
17. Fred
21. Antony
8. Bruno Fernandes (c)
10. Marcus Rashford
27. Wout Weghorst

Chapter 17

THE PREMIER LEAGUE ERA 1990's

RYAN GIGGS

1992-93

1. **Who were the first team that United faced in the newly formed Premier League?**
   a) Sheffield United b) Sheffield Wednesday c) Ipswich Town
   d) Blackburn Rovers

2. **How many matches did it take United to win their first game?**
   a) 2 b) 3 c) 4 d) 6

3. **United went out in the first round of the UEFA cup on penalties to which Russian club?**
   a) Dynamo Moscow b) Torpedo Moscow c) Sprtek Moscow
   d) Lokomotiv Moscow

4. **Which United legend scored the first ever Premier League hatrick?**
   a) Mark Hughes b) Bryan McClair c) Eric Cantona d) Bryan Robson

5. **Which team knocked Man United out of the fifth round of the FA Cup with a 2-1 win?**
   a) Sheffield Wednesday b) Sheffield United c) Burnely d) Everton

6. **Manchester United won the league that season by how many points?**
   a) 2 b) 5 c) 10 d) 13

7. **Which team came second?**
   a) Blackburn Rovers b) Norwich City c) Aston Villa d) Arsenal

8. **Who was the club's top goalscorer that season, with 16 goals in all competitions?**
   a) Dion Dublin b) Mark Hughes c) Ryan Giggs d) Bryan Robson

9. **Which United player was voted PFA young player of the year for the second season in a row?**
   a) Andy Cole b) Paul Scholes c) Ryan Giggs d) David Beckham

10. **Two players started every one of United's 50 games that season. Steve Bruce and who?**
    a) Ryan Giggs b) Peter Schmeichel c) Paul Parker d) Gary Palister

Answers: Page 198

1993-94
THE DOUBLE

1. Which team did United beat on penalties in the charity shield?
   a) Arsenal b) Liverpool c) Aston Villa d) Chelsea

2. The first and second league defeats United suffered were against the same opponents, who?
   a) Arsenal b) Leeds United c) Everton d) Chelsea

3. Which team, led by former manager Ron Atkinson, prevented United from becoming the first team to win the domestic treble, by beating them 3-1 in the League Cup final?
   a) Aston Villa b) Everton c) Sheffield Wednesday d) Leicester City

4. What colour was the third kit that season?
   a) Black b) Yellow and Green c) White d) Grey

5. Which United player was sent off that day?
   a) Lee Sharpe b) Paul Ince c) Steve Bruce d) Andrei Kanchelskis

6. "Welcome to Hell" banners were held up by fans of which team who knocked Manchester United out of the Champions League?
   a) Dinamo Moscow b) Red Star Belgrade c) Galatasaray d) Panathinaikos

7. Who scored twice from the penalty spot in Manchester United's 4-0 FA Cup final win over Chelsea, to help the club win their first domestic double?
   a) Eric Cantona b) Dennis Irwin c) Mark Hughes d) Brian McClair

8. Manchester United won the Premier League again that season. How many points did they win it by?
   a) 4 b) 6 c) 8 d) 10

9. Which team were runners up?
   a) Blackburn Rovers b) Aston Villa c) Newcastle United d) Liverpool

10. Which player was top goalscorer that season with 25 goals in all competitions?
    a) Mark Hughes b) Eric Cantona c) Brian McClair d) Lee Sharpe

Answers: Page 198

1994-95
THE DOUBLE

1. As United had won the double the previous season, who did they play in the Charity Shield?
   a) Liverpool b) Newcastle United c) Blackburn Rovers
   d) Manchester United reserves

2. Who was Manchester United's top scorer that season with 15 goals in all competitions?
   a) Brian McClair b) Andrei Kanchelskis c) Andy Cole
   d) Mark Hughes

3. Who was Ipswich Town's goalkeeper when Manchester United hammered them 9-0 at Old trafford?
   a) Mark Crossley b) Craig Forrest c) Kevin Poole d) Nigel Spink

4. Which United player scored five goals in that game?
   a) Mark Hughes b) Andy Cole c) Andrei Kanchelskis d) Andy Cole

5. Who knocked United out of the League Cup in the fourth round?
   a) Newcastle United b) Port Vale c) Norwich City d) Crystal Palace

6. United were knocked out in the group stages of the Champions League after coming third behind Barcelona and which other team?
   a) IFK Göteborg b) Hajduk Split c) Galatasaray d) Ajax

7. Who scored their first United goal in the final group game of the Champions League?
   a) Paul Scholes b) Gary Neville c) Keith Gillespie d) David Beckham

8. Manchester United drew 1-1 with which team on the final day, handing the title to Blackburn Rovers
   a) Aston Villa b) Tottenham Hotspur c) Wimbledon d) West Ham United

9. By how many points did Blackburn win the league that season?
   a) 1 b) 2 c) 3 d) 4

10. To finish off a disappointing season, United lost the FA Cup final 1-0 to which team?
    a) Leeds United b) Nottingham Forest c) Everton d) Liverpool

Answers: Page 198

1995-96

1. Who said "You can't win anything with kids!" after Manchester United's 3-1 loss to Aston Villa on the opening day?
   a) Mark Lawrenson b) Jimmy Hill c) Gary Lineker d) Alan Hansen

2. When 3-0 down at half-time to Southampton, Manchester United changed from their grey kit to which colour for the second half?
   a) Black b) Green & Yellow c) Blue & White d) White

3. Which team, that finished 64 places below United that season, caused a major upset when they knocked them out in the second round of the league cup?
   a) York City b) Wrexham c) Swindon Town d) Gillingham

4. King Cantona returned after his suspension and scored and got an assist in a 2-2 draw at Old Trafford against which team?
   a) Arsenal b) Liverpool c) Newcastle d) Blackburn Rovers

5. What was the name of Man United's FA Cup final single that season?
   a) "We're Gonna Do It Again" b) "United We Love You"
   c) "Come On You Reds" d) "Move Move Move"

6. Who was top goalscorer that season with 19 goals in all competitions?
   a) Eric Cantona b) Ryan Giggs c) Andy Cole d) Paul Scholes

7. Who had a 12-point lead in January but finished four points behind United?
   a) Liverpool b) Newcastle United c) Arsenal d) Aston Villa

8. Which team did United beat 3-0 on the final day of the season to win the title?
   a) Coventry City b) QPR c) Middlesbrough d) Swindon

9. Who scored in Manchester United's 1-0 FA Cup final win over Liverpool, to help the club win their second domestic double?
   a) David Beckham b) Eric Cantona c) Andy Cole d) Paul Scholes

10. Only two Manchester United players were included in Terry Venables' Euro 96 squad. Gary Neville and who else?
    a) David Beckham b) Paul Scholes c) Phil Neville d) Andy Cole

Answers: Page 198

1996-97

1. Which team did United smash 4-0 in the Charity Shield?
   a) Newcastle United b) Arsenal c) Liverpool d) Everton

2. Beckham scored a wodner goal on the opening day of the season, then ended as the club's third top goalscorer with how many goals?
   a) 18 b) 15 c) 12 d) 9

3. After a memorable performance at Euro 96, from which club did United sign Karel Poborsky?
   a) Viktoria Plzen b) Slovan Bratislava c) Ferencvaros
   d) Slavia Praha

4. On 30th October 1996, United's unbeaten home record in Europe, dating back to when they first entered the tournament in 1956/57, ended against which club?
   a) Fenerbahce b) Galatasaray c) Porto d) Rangers

5. In the group stages of the Champions League United were beaten 1-0 home and away by which defending champions?
   a) Juventus b) AC Milan c) Barcelona d) Real Madrid

6. They were knocked out of the Champions League in the semi-finals by which club that went on to lift the trophy?
   a) Porto b) Atlético Madrid c) Borussia Dortmund d) Ajax

7. With 19 goals in all competitions, who was United's top scorer?
   a) Andy Cole b) Ole Gunnar Solskjaer c) Eric Cantona
   d) Jordi Cruyff

8. United won the League for the 4th time in 5 years. Who was second?
   a) Newcastle United b) Arsenal c) Liverpool d) Blackburn Rovers

9. Manchester United's points total for this season is the lowest ever by the Premier League champions, how many points did they get?
   a) 73 b) 75 c) 77 d) 79

10. On 12th April 1997 Eric Cantona scored his last ever goal for the club in a 3-2 victory against which team?
    a) Blackburn Rovers b) Leicester City c) Derby County
    d) Southampton

Answers: Page 198

1997-98

1. What was the transfer fee Manchester United paid Tottenham Hotspur for Teddy Sheringham?
   a) £2 million b) £2.5 million c) £3 million d) £3.5 million

2. Which defender scored his first goal for the club in a 3-0 win over Košice in the Champions League?
   a) Ronny Johnsen b) David May c) Henning Berg d) Denis Irwin

3. United's biggest win of the season was a 7-0 victory of which team?
   a) Barnsley b) Derby County c) Coventry City d) Ipswich

4. The only hat-trick of the season was scored by which player?
   a) Teddy Sheringham b) Andy Cole c) Ole Gunnar Solskjaer
   d) Paul Scholes

5. United knocked Chelsea out of the FA Cup in the Third Round by what scoreline?
   a) 5-0 b) 5-1 c) 5-2 d) 5-3

6. United lost on away goals in the Champions League Quarter-finals to which team?
   a) Bayer Leverkusen b) Fenerbahce c) Juventus d) Monaco

7. United failed to win the title for only the second time in the Premier League era, finishing how many points behind Arsenal?
   a) 1 b) 2 c) 3 d) 4

8. What was done prematurely as United held an 11-point lead over Arsenal?
   a) Bookmakers paid out on United winning the title
   b) United's name was engraved on the trophy
   c) The Premier League sent winners' medals to Old Trafford
   d) The Prime Minister congratulated United on another title success

9. Karel Poborsky left midway through the season to join which team?
   a) FC Schalke 04 b) Ajax c) Real Sociedad d) Benfica

10. Who was United's top scorer in the league with 15 goals?
    a) Andy Cole b) Teddy Sheringham c) Ole Gunnar Solskjaer
    d) Ryan Giggs

Answers: Page 198

1998-99
THE TREBLE

1. On September 10th 1998, three years before any other club, Manchester United did what?
   a) Had a third team kit   b) Started their own TV channel, MUTV
   c) Sewed data sensors in the player's kits   d) Introduced a vegan diet

2. Which television broadcaster tried to buy the club that season?
   a) Santana   b) BskyB   c) Eurosport   d) BT Sport

3. How many goals did strike-partners Andy Cole and Dwight Yorke score in the 1998-99 season combined?
   a) 41   b) 48   c) 51   d) 53

4. How many matches did United lose after Christmas?
   a) 0   b) 1   c) 2   d) 3

5. That season, who became the first player to win the Premier League with two different clubs?
   a) Teddy Sheringham   b) Andy Cole   c) Henning Berg   d) Jordi Cruyff

6. Which team did United not beat en route to winning the FA Cup?
   a) Liverpool   b) Arsenal   c) Chelsea   d) Tottenham Hotspur

7. United beat Arsenal to the League title by how many points?
   a) 1   b) 2   c) 4   d) 6

8. Which Polish side did United beat in the second qualifying round of the Champions League?
   a) Lech Poznań   b) Legia Warszawa   c) LKS Lodz   d) Wisła Płock

9. United beat Bayern Munich 2-1 in the final of the Champions League to win the first ever treble. Who scored the winner?
   a) Teddy Sheringham   b) Ole Gunnar Solskjaer   c) Nicky Butt
   d) Ryan Giggs

10. Complete the quotation from Sir Alex Ferguson, speaking moments after winning the Champions League final and completing a historic treble: "Football...
    a) ...you can't beat it!"   b) ...what a game!"
    c) ...the best thing in life!"   d) ...bloody hell!"

Answers: Page 199

1999-00

1. Which side beat United 1-0 in the Super Cup final?
   a) Lazio b) Roma c) AC Milan d) Inter Milan

2. In November, Manchester United beat which team 1-0 to become England's first winners of the Intercontinental Cup?
   a) River Plate b) Corinthians c) Vasco da Gama d) Palmeiras

3. The club withdrew from which competition to play in the Club World Cup?
   a) League Cup b) FA Cup c) Charity Shield d) Champions League

4. Their only victory in the Club World Cup came against which team?
   a) South Melbourne b) Necaxa c) Al-Nassr d) Raja Casablanca

5. Which colour was added to the crest of the red shirt United played in for their Champions League matches that season?
   a) Gold b) Yellow c) Green d) Blue

6. Four goalkeepers made league appearances as Manchester United struggled to replace Peter Schmeichel. They were Mark Bosnich, Raimond van der Gouw, Nick Culkin and who?
   a) Paul Rachubka b) Fabien Barthez c) Andy Goram
   d) Massimo Taibi

7. Andy Cole and Ole Gunnar Solskjaer both did what as United retained the Premier League title?
   a) Score 20 goals b) Score 4 in one match c) Miss the entire season through injury d) Score in 5 straight games

8. Which player was United's leading goalscorer with 24 goals in all competitions?
   a) Dwight Yorke b) Andy Cole d) Ryan Giggs d) Paul Scholes

9. Which side knocked Man Utd out of the Champions League that season on their way to lifting the trophy?
   a) Barcelona b) Real Madrid c) Valencia d) Atletico Madrid

10. United won the league that season by how many points over Arsenal?
    a) 10 b) 15 c) 18 d) 21

195

Answers: Page 199

FUN FACTS, STORIES AND STATS

1. In the years prior to the establishment of the Premier League in 1992, English club football was in a difficult place. There were record low attendances, widespread fan hooliganism and TV coverage was rare. The Premier League changed English football by rejuvenating the love of the game as a spectator sport. Viewing figures of live broadcasts increased as did and attendances at live matches. Now, 30 years later, some weekends draw in just shy of half a million football fans to live games across the United Kingdom.

2. Three months before joining Manchester United Eric Cantona had begun the 1992-93 season with a hatrick for the league champions Leeds United against Liverpool in the Charity Shield. Two weeks later he scored the first hat-trick in the Premeier League against Tottenham Hopspur. However, despite this, his relationship with the club's managers Howard Wilkinson was turning sour due to Cantona's volatile and unpredictable personality. After only nine months at Leeds and already at his seventh club aged only 26, Cantona was bought by Manchester United for £1.2million. That season he scored nine goals and helped United win their first leaguue title in 26 years.

3. In 1994 the Manchester United squad recorded the song "Come on you reds." It was written and produced by the rock group Status Quo. It spent 15 weeks in the charts, two weeks of which were as the UK's number one single. They were knocked off the top by, "Love is All Around", by Wet Wet Wet.

4. On 30th October 1996, United's 40-year-old, 56-match unbeaten home record in Europe finally came to an end after Bosnian Elvir Bolic's late winning goal gave Fenerbahce a famous victory in the Champions League knock-out stages.

5. United were losing 1-0 to Tottenham Hotspur on the final game of the 1999 Premier League season. If the scores stayed that way Arsenal would be crowned champions. However David Beckham equalized just before half time and Andy Cole scored the winner in the second half.

6. United beat Chelsea 4-0 in the 1994 FA Cup final to win the clubs first league and cup double. The club would go on to win two more in the 90's. Wining it in 1995-96 and again in 1998-99. The season where they would go on to also win the Champions League, becoming the first and only English club to the League, Cup and European Treble. Arsenal are the only other club to win the double on three occasions. Winning it in 1970-71, 1997-98 and 2001-02.

7. Eric Cantona scored a superb volley from outside the area in a 1-0 win over local rivals Liverpool in the 1996 FA Cup final at Wembley. It was an inspirational goal from what is known by many as the 'Cantona Final.' It gave United their second domestic double in three years.

8. In May 1997, United won their fourth League title of the decade. It was to be Cantona's last, as he surprisingly retired from football that summer. He left a huge void in the squad and with Injuries to key players like Giggs and Roy Keane they won nothing in 1997/98, while Arsenal won the Double.

9. Ryan Giggs' goal in the 1999 FA Cup semi-final replay against Arsenal was perhaps the goal of the decade. His solo run ripped apart the Arsenal defence before he smashes it into the net. His celebration has become almost as famous, as he tore his shirt off and swung it around his head as he ran along the touchline. The goal booked the clubs place in their fifth FA Cup final of the 1990s, and goals by Paul Scholes and substitute Teddy Sheringham sealed a 2-0 against Newcastle, giving the their third domestic double of the decade

10. In the 1999/00 season Manchester United withdrew from the FA Cup so they could compete in the 2000 FIFA Club World Championship in South America. The tournament took place during the FA Cup third round in early 2000. The club became the first FA Cup winners not to defend their title. United went crashing out of the tournament in the group stages after a 2-0 win against Australian side South Melbourne, a 1-1 draw with Mexican side Metaxa and a 3-1 loss to Brazilian side Vasco de Gama.

TRIVIA QUIZ ANSWERS
Chapter 17: The Premier League Era - 1990's

1992-93
1. a) Sheffield United
2. c) 4
3. b) Torpedo Moscow
4. c) Eric Cantona
5. b) Sheffield United
6. c) 10
7. c) Aston Villa
8. b) Mark Hughes
9. c) Ryan Giggs
10. d) Gary Pallister

1993-94 - THE DOUBLE
1. a) Arsenal
2. d) Chelsea
3. a) Aston Villa
4. b) Yellow and Green
5. d) Andrei Kanchelskis
6. c) Galatasaray
7. a) Eric Cantona
8. c) 8
9. a) Blackburn Rovers
10. b) Eric Cantona

1994-95
1. c) Blackburn Rovers
2. b) Andrei Kanchelskis
3. b) Craig Forrest
4. d) Andy Cole
5. a) Newcastle United
6. a) IFK Göteborg
7. d) David Beckham
8. d) West Ham United
9. a) 1
10. c) Everton

1995-96 - THE DOUBLE
1. d) Alan Hansen
2. c) Blue & White
3. a) York City
4. b) Liverpool
5. d) "Move Move Move"
6. a) Eric Cantona
7. b) Newcastle United
8. c) Middlesbrough
9. b) Eric Cantona
10. c) Phil Neville

1996-97
1. a) Newcastle United
2. c) 12
3. d) Slavia Praha
4. a) Fenerbahce
5. a) Juventus
6. c) Borussia Dortmund
7. b) Ole Gunnar Solskjaer
8. a) Newcastle United
9. b) 75
10. a) Blackburn Rovers

1997-98
1. d) £3.5 million
2. c) Henning Berg
3. a) Barnsley
4. b) Andy Cole
5. d) 5-3
6. d) Monaco
7. a) 1
8. a) Bookmakers paid out on United winning the title
9. d) Benfica
10. a) Andy Cole

1998-99 - THE TREBLE

1. b) Started their own TV channel, MUTV
2. b) BskyB
3. d) 53
4. a) 0
5. c) Henning Berg
6. d) Tottenham Hotspur
7. a) 1
8. c) LKS Lodz
9. b) Ole Gunnar Solskjaer
10. d) ...bloody hell!"

1999-00

1. a) Lazio
2. d) Palmeiras
3. b) FA Cup
4. a) South Melbourne
5. a) Gold
6. d) Massimo Taibi
7. b) Score 4 in one match
8. a) Dwight Yorke
9. b) Real Madrid
10. c) 18

Chapter 18
THE PREMIER LEAGUE ERA
2000's

EDWIN
VAN DER SAR

2000-01

1. Fabien Barthez was Manchester United's only arrival all season, joining for £7.8m from which club?
   a) Marseille b) Monaco c) Nantes d) Lens

2. United lost their last three games of the season and finished where?
   a) First b) Second c) Third d) Fourth

3. Who was the top goalscorer with 21 goals in all competitions?
   a) Teddy Sheringham b) Andy Cole c) Dwight Yorke d) Ryan Giggs

4. Who scored the goal for West Ham United that knocked United out of the FA Cup?
   a) Trevor Sinclair b) Freddie Kanoute c) Paolo Di Canio
   d) Jermain Defoe

5. Which round of the FA Cup was it?
   a) 3rd b) 4th c) 5th d) Quarterfinals

6. Sir Alex Ferguson missed United's 1-0 away win over Manchester City in the Premier League so he could attend the wedding of his son. Who took charge in his place?
   a) Michael Carrick b) Jimmy Ryan c) Carlos Queiroz
   d) Steve McClaren

7. Roy Keane was openly critical of the home fans' support. Which type of sandwiches did he say they ate?
   a) BLT b) Prawn c) Avocado d) Salmon

8. Which player won the PFA and Football Writers' Player of the Year?
   a) Paul Scholes b) Ryan Giggs c) David Beckham
   d) Teddy Sheringham

9. Which team knocked United out of the Champions League?
   a) Bayern Munich b) Juventus c) AC Milan d) Barcelona

10. Manchester United again won their 7th Premier League title that season by how many points?
    a) 5 b) 10 c) 15 d) 20

Answers: Page 214

2001-02

1. **United lost the Charity Shield for the fourth season in a row to whom?**
   a) Chelsea   b) Arsenal   c) Aston Villa   d) Liverpool

2. **Which player did United sign from Lazio, for a then British record transfer fee of £28.1 million?**
   a) Juan Sebastian Veron   b) Diago Forlan   c) Louis Saha   d) Kleberson

3. **Manchester United beat Tottenham Hotspur 5-3 in September. What was the half-time score?**
   a) 0-0   b) 3-0 to Tottenham   c) 5-0 to United   d) 2-0 to Tottenham

4. **How many goals did Van Nistelrooy score in all competitions in his debut season?**
   a) 24   b) 28   c) 32   d) 36

5. **Van Nistelrooy's first United hat-trick was in a 6-1 win over who?**
   a) Derby County   b) Everton   c) Bournemouth   d) Southampton

6. **For only the second time in the Premier League era, United failed to do what?**
   a) Win the title   b) Win a trophy   c) Finish in the top two
   d) Reach the Champions LeagueQuarter-Finals

7. **Their third place league finish was their lowest since when?**
   a) 1988   b) 1989   c) 1991   d) 1992

8. **Despite that, they were the Premier League's highest scorers with how many goals?**
   a) 81   b) 83   c) 85   d) 87

9. **Ironically, what was the main colour of their third kit, which also featured on their away kit?**
   a) Gold   b) Blue   c) Red   d) Silver

10. **How many times did Manchester United face Deportivo La Coruña in the Champions League?**
    a) 1   b) 2   c) 3   d) 4

Answers: Page 214

2002-03

1. United went on an incredible unbeaten run after Boxing Day. How many games was it?
   a) 14 b) 16 c) 18 d) 20

2. What colour was the away kit that season?
   a) White Yellow c) Black d) Blue

3. Who was the Manchester United goalkeeper that season?
   a) Fabien Barthez b) Massimo Taibi c) Raymond van der Gouw
   d) Tim Howard

4. Which team did they destroy 6-0 in the FA Cup 4th round that season?
   a) Doncaster Rovers b) Arsenal c) Blackburn Rovers
   d) West Ham United

5. After initially struggling in England, who scored twice at Anfield in a 2-1 win over Liverpool?
   a) Juan Sebastian Veron b) Diego Forlan c) Mikael Silvestre
   d) Quinton Fortune

6. A hat-trick from which Real Madrid player at Old Trafford knocked Manchester United out of the Champions League?
   a) Raul b) Fernando Morientes c) Zinedine Zidane d) Ronaldo

7. Old Trafford hosted the 2003 Champions League final between which two clubs?
   a) Real Madrid & Valencia b) Milan & Bayer Leverkusen c) Milan & Juventus
   d) Real Madrid & Juventus

8. What was the score in that game?
   a) 0-0 b) 1-1 c) 2-2 d) 3-3

9. Ruud Van Nistelrooy was Manchester United's leading goalscorer that season. He played 52 times. How many goals did he score?
   a) 29 b) 34 c) 38 d) 44

10. United won the title by how many points that season?
    a) 5 b) 8 c) 11 d) 14

Answers: Page 214

2003-04

1. Which team did United beat 4-3 on penalties in that season's Charity Shield?
   a) Chelsea b) Liverpool c) Arsenal d) Newcastle

2. Cristiano Ronaldo signed in August, who else signed that day?
   a) Louis Saha b) Tim Howard c) David Bellion d) Kleberson

3. How many goals did Cristiano Ronaldo score in all competitions in this, his debut season?
   a) 4 b) 6 c) 8 d) 10

4. What colour was the away kit that season?
   a) Blue b) Black c) Yellow d) Green

5. Juan Sebastián Verón left United that season to join which Premier League side for £15 million?
   a) Chelsea b) Tottenham Hotspur c) West Ham d) Liverpool

6. United were knocked out of the Champions League by the eventual winners. Who were they?
   a) Monaco b) AC Milan c) Real Madrid d) Porto

7. Which team knocked United out of the League Cup?
   a) West Brom b) Birmingham City c) Leicester City
   d) Derby County

8. Who did Manchester United beat 3-0 in the FA Cup final?
   a) Southampton b) Bolton Wanderers c) Millwall d) Middlesbrough

9. Ruud Van Nistelrooy was top goalscorer again that season with how goals?
   a) 26 b) 30 c) 35 d) 37

10. United finished third in the league, how many points behind invincible champions, Arsenal?
    a) 9 b) 12 c) 15 d) 18

Answers: Page 214

2004-05

1. Manchester United's opening game of the season was the first in English football for which opposition manager?
   a) Jose Mourinho b) Rafael Benitez c) Alain Perrin d) Martin Jol

2. Which unlikely hero scored twice in a 2-1 win over Liverpool in September?
   a) John O'Shea b) Gerard Pique c) Wes Brown d) Mikael Silvestre

3. United ended Arsenal's unbeaten Premier League run at 49 games. Rooney and who else scored?
   a) Alan Smith b) Paul Scholes c) Ruud van Nistelrooy
   d) Cristiano Ronaldo

4. Which side did United beat in the qualifying round of the Champions League?
   a) Celtic b) Dinamo Bucureşti c) Dynamo Kiev d) Steaua Bucureşti

5. Which Italian side knocked them out of the Champions League?
   a) AC Milan b) Inter Milan c) Lazio d) Roma

6. Who was named PFA young player of the year that season?
   a) Wayne Rooney b) Christiano Ronaldo c) Nani d) Kleberson

7. On their to the FA Cup final that season, United had to overcome which non-league side in the FA Cup 3rd round after a 0-0 draw at Old Trafford?
   a) Burton Albion b) Gillingham c) Wrexham d) Exeter City

8. United lost the FA Cup final on penalties to which team?
   a) Liverpool b) Chelsea c) Manchester City d) Arsenal

9. Chelsea won the Premier League that season. What position did Man Utd finish?
   a) 2nd b) 3rd c) 4th d) 5th

10. Who was United's top goalscorer that season with 19 goals?
    a) Cristiano Ronaldo b) Wayne Rooney c) Ruud Van Nistelrooy
    d) Paul Scholes

Answers: Page 214

2005-06

1. **Who scored Manchester United's 1000th Premier League goal in a 4-1 loss to Middlesbrough?**
a) Wayne Rooney b) Cristiano Ronaldo c) Ruud van Nistelrooy
d) Louis Saha

2. **MUTV was pulled from transmission after Roy Keane criticised which teammate live on air?**
a) Alan Smith b) Darren Fletcher c) Kieran Richardson
d) Rio Ferdinand

3. **What colour was the away shirt that season?**
a) Blue b) Black c) Grey d) Gold

4. **Manchester United beat which team 4-0 in the League Cup final?**
a) Sunderland b) Derby County c) Wigan Athletic d) Reading

5. **Which side did United beat in the qualifying round of the Champions League?**
a) Debrecen b) Lille c) Panathinaikos d) FC Basel

6. **Which non-league side took Man Utd to a replay after a 0-0 draw in the FA Cup 3rd round, before being beaten 5-0 at Old Trafford?**
a) Burton Albion b) Kidderminster Harriers c) Crawly Town
d) Woking

7. **Which side knocked United out of the FA Cup after beating the 1-0 away in the 5th round?**
a) Arsenal b) Chelsea c) Liverpool d) Everton

8. **What did Manchester United do for the first time in the Champions League?**
a) Be eliminated in qualification b) Fail to win a match
c) Finish bottom of the group d) Fail to score at home

9. **What position did United finish in the Premier League that season behind Chelsea?**
a) Second b) Third c) Fourth d) Fifth

10. **Who was the top goalscorer in all competitions with 24?**
a) Ruud Van Nistelrooy b) Luis Saha c) Cristiano Ronaldo

Answers: Page 214

2006-07

1. Henrick Larsson scored the first United goal of his short spell in the FA Cup Third Round against who?
   a) Watford b) Portsmouth c) Middlesbrough d) Aston Villa

2. Who did United beat 7-1 in the Champions League, their biggest win in all competitions?
   a) Roma b) FC Copenhagen c) Celtic d) Benfica

3. For how many rounds of fixtures did Manchester United not sit at the top of the Premier League?
   a) 2 b) 5 c) 7 d) 8

4. Who scored the only goal as Manchester United lost to Chelsea 1-0 in the first FA Cup final at the new Wembley?
   a) Frank Lampard b) Michael Essien c) Didier Drogba d) Joe Cole

5. Rooney and Ronaldo ended the season joint top goalscorers in all competitions with how many goals each?
   a) 19 b) 23 c) 25 d) 29

6. Which player made his 500th appearance for the club that season, in a 2-0 win against Liverpool at Old Trafford?
   a) Ryan Giggs b) Paul Scholes c) David Beckham d) Nicky Butt

7. Which team knocked United out of the champions league in the semi-final with a 5-3 win on aggregate?
   a) AC Milan Liverpool c) Chelsea d) Bayern Munich

8. Two teams beat United home and away that season. Arsenal were one of them, who was the other?
   a) Tottenham Hotspur b) Chelsea c) West Ham d) Crystal Palace

9. United won the Premier League that season. Who finished second?
   a) Arsenal b) Chelsea c) Liverpool d) Man City

10. Who won the PFA Player of the Year award for the first time?
    a) Ryan Giggs b) Cristiano Ronaldo c) Nemanja Vidic
    d) Wayne Rooney

2007-08
THE DOUBLE

1. Which team completed a double over United in the match to commemorate the 50th anniversary of the Munich Air Disaster?
   a) Chelsea b) Newcastle United c) Portsmouth d) Manchester City

2. The club did something special, what was it?
   a) Let off 1000 red balloons b) Put Bobby Charlton on the bench
   c) Wore the 1958 jersey d) Invited the families onto the pitch

3. Cristiano Ronaldo scored how many goals that season in all competitions?
   a) 31 b) 37 c) 42 d) 46

4. The club played their 5,000th competitive match, in a 1-0 win over which team in the Champions League?
   a) AC Milan b) Inter Milan c) Fiorentia d) Napoli

5. United smashed which team 6-0 that season, thanks to a hat-trick from Cristiano Ronaldo?
   a) Southampton b) Manchester United c) Liverpool
   d) Newcastle United

6. United won the title on the final day with a 2-0 win over which club?
   a) Blackburn Rovers b) Wigan Athletic c) Bolton Wanderers
   d) Aston Villa

7. Manchester United won their 10th Premier League title that season, how many points did they finish above Chelsea?
   a) 1 b) 2 c) 3 d) 4

8. How many Champions League matches did Manchester United lose en route to winning a third European Cup?
   a) 0 b) 1 c) 2 d) 3

9. What was the score in the penalty shootout as Man United beat Chelsea in the final?
   a) 4-3 b) 5-4 c) 6-5 d) 7-6

10. Who was the only United player to miss a penalty in the final?
    a) Rooney b) Ronaldo c) Giggs d) Scholes

Answers: Page 215

2008-09

1. United beat which team 1-0 in the final of the Club World Cup?
   a) Flamengo b) Colo-Colo c) Vélez Sarsfield d) LDU Quito

2. United played which team in the UEFA Super Cup?
   a) Dinamo Moscow b) Shakhtar Donetsk c) Zenit St Petersburg
   d) BATE Borisov

3. Who signed for United from Partizan Belgrade in January?
   a) Bojan Djordjic b) Nemanja Vidic c) Zoran Tosic
   d) Vanja Milinkovic-Savic

4. Edwin van der Sar broke the record for most minutes without conceding a goal in English football. How many minutes did he keep a clean sheet for?
   a) 998 b) 1,100 c) 1,311 d) 1,521

5. United lost just four times on their way to winning their third-straight Premier League title. Which club did the double over them?
   a) Fulham b) Arsenal c) Aston Villa d) Liverpool

6. United won two other pieces of domestic silverware, both on penalties after goalless finals. What were they?
   a) Community Shield & League Cup b) League Cup & FA Cup
   c) FA Cup & Super Cup d) Super Cup & Community Shield

7. Which player was named PFA Player of the Year that season?
   a) Paul Scholes b) Cristiano Ronaldo c) Ryan Giggs d) Dimitar Berbatov

8. United topped their Champions League group, how many of their six group games did they win?
   a) 1 b) 2 c) 3 d) 4

9. United beat who in an all-English Champions League semi-final?
   a) Arsenal b) Liverpool c) Chelsea d) Tottenham Hotspur

10. Lionel Messi and who else scored for Barcelona in the Champions League final as they beat United 2-0?
    a) Thierry Henry b) Andres Iniesta c) Samuel Eto'o d) Carles Puyol

Answers: Page 215

2009-10

1. Cristiano Ronaldo joined Real Madrid in the summer for what transfer fee?
   a) £70m b) £80m c) £90m d) £100m

2. From which club did Gabriel Obertan arrive?
   a) Bordeaux b) Troyes c) Stade Rennais d) Caen

3. Which newly-promoted team beat Manchester United 1-0 in August?
   a) Burnley b) Stoke City c) Hull City d) Southampton

4. Michael Owen scored a 96th-minute winner as United won the Manchester derby 4-3, but who scored twice in that game?
   a) Michael Carrick b) Darren Fletcher c) Antonio Valencia
   d) Park Ji-Sung

5.
   The other Manchester derby also saw United score an injury-time winner? Who grabbed that goal?
   a) Ryan Giggs b) Danny Welbeck c) Paul Scholes
   d) Owen Hargreaves

6. United missed out on the title for the first time since 2006, how many points did they finish behind Chelsea?
   a) 0 (finished second on goal difference) b) 1 c) 2 d) 3

7. Wayne Rooney and who else scored as Manchester United beat Aston Villa 2-1 in the League Cup final?
   a) Dimitar Berbatov b) Mame Biram Diouf c) Michael Owen
   d) Danny Welbeck

8. What was the aggregate score when United beat Milan in the first knockout round of the Champions League?
   a) 5-1 b) 6-0 c) 7-2 d) 8-3

9. A memorable volley from whom helped Bayern Munich knock United out of the Champions League?
   a) Ivica Olic b) Franck Ribery c) Mark van Bommel d) Arjen Robben

10. Rooney had his joint-best goal-scoring season. How many did he score in all competitions?
    a) 33 b) 34 c) 35 d) 36

Answers: Page 215

FUN FACTS, STORIES AND STATS

1. In 2000-01 Sir Alex Ferguson became the first manager to win three league titles in a row. The club won their 14th title that season which put them four behind Liverpool's record of 19. When Sir Alex Ferguson joined the club his goal was to beat Liverpool's record.

2. In November 2000, after a nervy 1-0 win over Dynamo Kiev at Old Trafford, Roy Keane infamously attacked the home fans. He felt the result had been achieved despite of them, rather than because of them. "We're 1-0 up, then there are one or two stray passes and they're getting on players' backs. It's just not on. They need to get behind the team. Away from home our fans are fantastic, I'd call them the hardcore fans. But at home, they have a few drinks and probably the prawn sandwiches, and they don't realise what's going on out on the pitch. I don't think some of the people who come to Old Trafford can spell 'football', never mind understand it."

3. In the summer of 2002 United signed Rio Ferdinand, one of England's best performers at the World Cup in Japan and Korea. He was bought for £30million from Leeds United and added the stability that had been missing from United's defence since the controversial departure of Jaap Stam to Lazio in 2001 Ferdinand helped the Reds to win the Premier league title in 2003.

4. David Beckham left his longtime home by in 2003 when he signed for Real Madrid's Galacticos. He teamed up with players like Roberto Carlos, Ronaldo, Raúl, Luís Figo and went on to win one La Liga championship and a Spanish Super Cup

5. Arsenal's invincibles won the 2003-04 Premeier Leaguem going the whole season unbeaten. But United won the 2004 FA Cup for an 11th time, beating Millwall 3-0 in the final at Cardiff's Millennium Stadium

6. When Ronaldo signed for Manchester United in 2003 he requested the number 28 shirt but Sir Alex Ferguson refused. He suggested that he wear the number 7 shirt. The number came with certain pressures and expectations as it had been worn by numerous legends before him. Ronaldo stepped up to the challenge. He was 18 years old at the time.

7. On 10th February 2008 Manchester United marked the 50th anniversary of the Munich Air Disaster. The match was against Manchester City and the team's wore shirts designed to like those worn in 1958. There was a minute's silence before the game, which Manchester City won 2-1

8. In 2008 Manchestr United were kings of Europe for the third time in their history after ebating Chelsea on penalties in Moscow. A year later they reached teh final again, this against Barcelona in Rome. Barcelona won the match 2-0 thanks to goals by Samuel Eto'o and Lionel Messi.

9. Despite the loss in the champions League final, the 2008/09 season was incredible with the team winning the Premier League and League cup and the FIFA Club World Cup

10. In 2009, after the departure of Ronaldo to Real Madrid, Manchester United bought Antonio Valencia from Wigan Athletic. He was given the number 25 jersey and played for the club for the next ten years.

TRIVIA QUIZ ANSWERS
Chapter 18: The Premier League Era - 2000's

2000-01
1. b) Monaco
2. a) First
3. a) Teddy Sheringham
4. c) Paolo Di Canio
5. b) 4th
6. d) Steve McClaren
7. b) Prawn
8. d) Teddy Sheringham
9. a) Bayern Munich
10. b) 10

2001-02
1. d) Liverpool
2. a) Juan Sebastian Veron
3. b) 3-0 to Tottenham
4. d) 36
5. d) Southampton
6. b) Win a trophy
7. c) 1991
8. d) 87
9. a) Gold
10. d) 4

2002-03
1. c) 18
2. a) White
3. a) Fabien Barthez
4. d) West Ham United
5. b) Diego Forlan
6. d) Ronaldo
7. c) Milan & Juventus
8. a) 0-0
9. d) 44
10. a) 5

2003-04
1. c) Arsenal
2. d) Kleberson
3. b) 6
4. b) Black
5. a) Chelsea
6. d) Porto
7. a) West Brom
8. c) Millwall
9. b) 30
10. c) 15

2004-05
1. a) Jose Mourinho
2. d) Mikael Silvestre
3. c) Ruud van Nistelrooy
4. b) Dinamo București
5. a) AC Milan
6. a) Wayne Rooney
7. d) Exeter City
8. d) Arsenal
9. b) 3rd
10. b) Wayne Rooney

2005-06
1. b) Cristiano Ronaldo
2. d) Rio Ferdinand
3. a) Blue
4. c) Wigan Athletic
5. a) Debrecen
6. a) Burton Albion
7. c) Liverpool
8. c) Finish bottom of the group
9. a) Second
10. a) Ruud Van Nistelrooy

2006-07

1. d) Aston Villa
2. a) Roma
3. a) 2
4. c) Didier Drogba
5. b) 23
6. b) Paul Scholes
7. a) AC Milan
8. c) West Ham
9. b) Chelsea
10. b) Cristiano Ronaldo

2007-08 - THE DOUBLE

1. d) Manchester City
2. c) Wore the 1958 jersey
3. c) 42
4. a) AC Milan
5. d) Newcastle United
6. b) Wigan Athletic
7. b) 2
8. a) 0
9. c) 6-5
10. b) Ronaldo

2008-09

1. d) LDU Quito
2. c) Zenit St Petersburg
3. c) Zoran Tosic
4. c) 1,311
5. d) Liverpool
6. a) Community Shield & League Cup
7. c) Ryan Giggs
8. b) 2
9. a) Arsenal
10. c) Samuel Eto'o

2009-10

1. b) £80m
2. a) Bordeaux
3. a) Burnley
4. b) Darren Fletcher
5. c) Paul Scholes
6. b) 1
7. c) Michael Owen
8. c) 7-2
9. d) Arjen Robben
10. b) 34

Chapter 19
THE PREMIER LEAGUE ERA
2010's

2010-11

1. Javier Hernandez was signed in the summer from which club?
   a) UNAM b) Club América c) Guadalajara d) Cruz Azul

2. Dimitar Berbatov scored five times in a 7-1 win over whom?
   a) Derby County b) Stoke City c) Birmingham City
   d) Blackburn Rovers

3. What was the date of United's first league defeat? A 1-0 loss to Wolverhampton Wanderers?
   a) 14th November b) 1st December c) 20th January d) 5th February

4. Who scored their only United goals against Wolves in the League Cup and Bursaspor in the Champions League?
   a) Gabriel Obertan b) Darron Gibson c) Fabio d) Bebe

5. Which club stalwart retired in February?
   a) Gary Neville b) Ryan Giggs c) Paul Scholes d) Rio Ferdinand

6. Which rival knocked United out of the FA Cup at the semi-final stage?
   a) Arsenal b) Liverpool c) Manchester City d) Chelsea

7. United's 19th league title was confirmed with a 1-1 draw on the penultimate day of the season against who?
   a) Blackpool b) Fulham c) Everton d) Blackburn Rovers

8. Who did United beat 6-1 on aggregate in the Champions League semi-finals?
   a) Schalke 04 b) FC Porto c) Werder Bremen d) Bayer Leverkusen

9. Wayne Rooney scored in every round of the Champions League except which one?
   a) Group stage b) Last 16 c) Quarter-finals d) Semi-finals

10. United lost the Champions League final to Barcelona for the second time in three seasons. Where was the match held?
    a) Allianz Arena b) Luzhniki Stadium c) Stadio Olimpico
    d) Wembley Stadium

Answers: Page 230

2011-12

1. Manchester United smashed Arsenal at Old Trafford by what score?
   a) 6-0 b) 7-1 c) 8-2 d) 9-1

2. United's only league defeat before Christmas was a 1-6 loss to Manchester City? Who scored for the Red Devils?
   a) Dimitar Berbatov b) Javier Hernandez c) Anderson
   d) Darren Fletcher

3. Their only wins in the Champions League came against Oțelul Galați, who heralds from which country?
   a) Romania b) Ukraine c) Israel d) Bulgaria

4. Manchester United reached the Last 16 of the Europa League only to be knocked out by whom?
   a) Real Betis b) Real Sociedad c) Athletic Bilbao d) Rayo Vallecano

5. Who made their first seven appearances for the club from the substitutes bench?
   a) Tom Cleverly b) Paul Pogba c) Anders Lindegaard
   d) Michael Owen

6. After retiring the previous summer, who returned in January?
   a) Gary Neville b) Ryan Giggs c) Michael Owen d) Paul Scholes

7. The dramatic last-minute "Aguero Moment" denied United the title after a 1-0 win over whom on the final day of the season?
   a) Hull City b) Sunderland c) Stoke City d) Queens Park Rangers

8. The two Manchester clubs finished on 89 points. City's goal difference was +64, what was United's?
   a) +48 b) +56 c) +59 d) +63

9. Wayne Rooney was top scorer with 34 goals, how many did joint runners-up Javier Hernandez and Danny Welbeck each score?
   a) 12 b) 15 c) 17 d) 20

10. Seven United players went to Euro 2012; who got the furthest, reaching the semi-finals?
    a) Nani b) Patrice Evra c) Anders Lindegaard d) Wayne Rooney

Answers: Page 230

2012-13

1. Shinji Kagawa arrived at Old Trafford from which club?
   a) Borussia Dortmund b) FC Zürich c) Anderlecht d) Feyenoord

2. The home shirt that season paid tribute to what?
   a) The Munich Air Disaster b) The Manchester cotton industry
   c) The 1968 European Cup win d) The club's global fan base

3. Who scored their only Premier League goal for United on debut in a win over Wigan Athletic?
   a) Nick Powell b) Alex Büttner c) Scott Wootton d) Will Keane

4. As the only new arrival in January, who was the last player to join United in the Sir Alex Ferguson era?
   a) Angelo Henriquez b) Wilfried Zaha c) Frederic Veseli d) Alex Büttner

5. In the Champions League, Manchester United faced which former player for the first time since selling him?
   a) Paul Pogba b) Louis Saha c) Cristiano Ronaldo d) Gabriel Heinze

6. Which team knocked United out of both the FA and League Cup?
   a) Tottenham Hotspur b) Everton c) West Ham United d) Chelsea

7. Who scored a hat-trick to beat Aston Villa 3-0 and secure Sir Alex Ferguson's final Premier League title?
   a) Robin van Persie b) Javier Hernandez c) Dimitar Berbatov
   d) Wayne Rooney

8. How many goals in all competitions did Robin van Persie score in his debut campaign?
   a) 22 b) 26 c) 30 d) 34

9. Sir Alex's last home match and last win was a 2-1 victory over which side?
   a) Cardiff City b) Swansea City c) Reading d) Stoke City

10. United drew with West Bromwich Albion in Ferguson's last match in charge, what was the score?
    a) 2-2 b) 3-3 c) 4-4 d) 5-5

Answers: Page 230

2013-14

1. David Moyes became Manchester United manager after how many years at Everton?
   a) 7 b) 9 c) 11 d) 13

2. Who became the first signing of the post-Fergie era?
   a) Marouane Fellaini b) Saidy Janko c) Luke Shaw d) Guillermo Varela

3. Moyes' only silverware was the Community Shield, which United won with a 2-0 win against whom?
   a) Wigan Athletic b) Chelsea c) Arsenal d) Manchester City

4. Who scored twice on their Premier League debut in a 2-1 away win at Sunderland?
   a) Danny Welbeck b) Adnan Januzaj c) Tom Cleverley
   d) James Wilson

5. Who was United's only signing of the January transfer window?
   a) Juan Mata b) Marouane Fellaini c) Luke Shaw d) Ander Herrera

6. A Robin van Persie hat-trick in the Champions League Last 16 turned around a 2-0 first-leg loss to which club?
   a) Trabzonspor b) Dynamo Kiev c) APOEL Nicosia d) Olympiacos

7. Who did United lose to on pwenelties in the semi-finals of the League Cup?
   a) Manchester City b) Stoke City c) Liverpool d) Sunderland

8. Manchester United finished seventh in the Premier League; how many defeats did they suffer?
   a) 11 b) 12 c) 13 d) 14

9. United lost 2-0 to which team in Moyes' final match as manager?
   a) Aston Villa b) West Ham United c) Everton d) Hull City

10. Ryan Giggs took interim charge for the last four matches; who did United beat 4-0 in his first game?
    a) Hull City b) Newcastle United c) Aston Villa d) Norwich City

Answers: Page 230

2014-15

1. Louis van Gaal was confirmed as manager before the World Cup, where his Netherlands team finished in what place?
   a) 2nd b) 3rd c) 4th d) Quarter-finals

2. United lost their opening home game for the first time since when?
   a) 1998 b) 1991 c) 1984 d) 1972

3. Van Gaal's first win as Manchester United manager came after how many matches?
   a) 3 b) 4 c) 5 d) 6

4. Angel di Maria signed for £59.7m from which club?
   a) Benfica b) Paris Saint-Germain c) Juventus d) Real Madrid

5. United were knocked out of the League Cup 4-0 in the second round by whom?
   a) Oxford United b) Coventry City c) Gillingham d) MK Dons

6. Radamel Falcao scored how many goals during his season-long loan from Monaco?
   a) 4 b) 6 c) 8 d) 10

7. United reached the quarter-finals of the FA Cup and were knocked out by whom?
   a) Arsenal b) Chelsea c) Leicester City d) Everton

8. Which League Two side took them to a replay in the fourth round?
   a) Yeovil Town b) Cambridge United c) Stevenage d) Luton Town

9. Rooney was United's top scorer in the league again, how many did he score?
   a) 12 b) 15 c) 18 d) 20

10. With 70 points, where did United finish in the league?
    a) 3rd b) 4th c) 5th d) 6th

Answers: Page 230

2015-16

1. **Louis van Gaal signed Dutchman Memphis Depay from where?**
   a) Lyon b) Barcelona c) Feyenoord d) PSV Eindhoven

2. **Louis van Gaal tried to rally players and fans by chanting what in a pre-match press conference?**
   a) Glory Glory Man United b) Louis van Gaal's Army
   c) We Love United d) 12 Days of Cantona

3. **Which team did Manchester United beat 7-1 on aggregate in the Champions League play-offs?**
   a) Midtjylland b) IFK Goteborg c) Club Brugge d) Young Boys

4. **Who knocked United out of the Europa League?**
   a) Chelsea b) Bayern Munich c) Celtic d) Liverpool

5. **Who scored twice on their Premier League debut against Arsenal?**
   a) Marcus Rashford b) Anthony Martial c) Memphis Depay
   d) Adnan Januzaj

6. **With a only 11 goals, who was top scorer in the Premier League?**
   a) Memphis Depay b) Anthony Martial c) Juan Mata
   d) Wayne Rooney

7. **Who scored an extra-time winner in the FA Cup final against Crystal Palace?**
   a) Chris Smalling b) Juan Mata c) Juan Mata d) Jesse Lingard

8. **Why was the FA Cup success Louis van Gaal's last match?**
   a) He left due to health reasons b) He became Netherlands manager
   c) He was sacked d) He refused a new contract

9. **Who became the first player to win the Sir Matt Busby Player of the Year award for a third successive time?**
   a) David de Gea b) Wayne Rooney c) Luke Shaw d) Ashley Young

10. **The wife of which outgoing player said this about Manchester and England; "People are all weird. You walk around and you don't know if they're going to kill you. The food is disgusting. The women look like porcelain."**
    a) Robin van Persie b) Rafael c) Nani d) Angel di Maria

Answers: Page 230

2016-17

1. Jose Mourinho replaced Louis van Gaal as manager less than a year after being sacked by whom?
   a) Real Madrid b) Inter Milan c) Porto d) Chelsea

2. Manchester United broke the British transfer record to bring Paul Pogba back from Juventus for what fee?
   a) £82m b) £89m c) £91m d) £96m

3. Henrikh Mkhitaryan became United's first player from which country?
   a) Azerbaijan b) Moldova c) Iran d) Armenia

4. Who scored twice in the League Cup final as United beat Southampton 3-2?
   a) Henrikh Mkhitaryan b) Zlatan Ibrahimovic c) Antonio Valencia
   d) Anthony Martial

5. Rooney scored his final goal in May, in a 2-1 loss against whom?
   a) Southampton b) Tottenham Hotspur c) Swansea City d) Everton

6. Zlatan also finished as the club's top scorer with how many goals in all competitions?
   a) 22 b) 24 c) 26 d) 28

7. Which of these teams did United not beat en route to winning the Europa League?
   a) Celta Vigo b) Rostov c) Fenerbahçe d) Twente

8. The final against Ajax was played in the Friends Arena, Solna, on the outskirts of which city?
   a) Copenhagen b) Stockholm c) Oslo d) Helsinki

9. Paul Pogba and who else scored the goals in the 2-0 win over Ajax?
   a) Marcus Rashford b) Marouane Fellaini c) Juan Mata
   d) Henrikh Mkhitaryan

10. Where did United finish in the Premier League in Mourinho's first season as manager?
    a) 3rd b) 4th c) 5th d) 6th

Answers: Page 231

2017-18

1. **Manchester United lost the UEFA Super Cup 2-1 to Real Madrid. Where was the match played?**
   a) Tirana, Albania b) Tallinn, Estonia c) Tbilisi, Georgia
   d) Skopje, North Macedonia

2. **United didn't lose in the league until mid-October, which unlikely team was the first to beat them?**
   a) Bournemouth b) Huddersfield Town c) Burnley d) Stoke City

3. **In the Manchester derby, came back from 2-0 down at the Etihad to win 2-3, with who scoring the winning goal?**
   a) Nemanja Matic b) Romelu Lukaku c) Paul Pogba
   d) Chris Smalling

4. **Jose Mourinho would later say that what achievement from this season was his greatest in management?**
   a) Reaching the FA Cup final b) Finishing second c) Beating CSKA Moscow away d) Managing Marcos Rojo

5. **How many points did United finish behind champions Man City?**
   a) 6 b) 9 c) 16 d) 19

6. **In all competitions, United only once lost by more than one goal, to whom?**
   a) Sevilla b) FC Basel c) Newcastle United d) Tottenham Hotspur

7. **Who beat United 1-0 in the FA Cup final?**
   a) Chelsea b) Liverpool c) Arsenal d) Leicester City

8. **De Gea kept the most Premier League clean sheets that season with how many?**
   a) 14 b) 15 c) 18 d) 20

9. **Romelu Lukaku was United's top scorer with how many goals in all competitions in his debut season?**
   a) 22 b) 25 c) 27 d) 30

10. **Who was captain the side on the last day of the season as he retired?**
    a) Ashley Young b) Daley Blind c) Zlatan Ibrahimovic
    d) Michael Carrick

Answers: Page 231

2018-19

1. Fred arrived in the summer from which club?
   a) Schalke b) Shakhtar Donetsk c) Santos d) Sevilla

2. Manchester United were knocked out of the League Cup by Derby County. Who was the Rams' manager?
   a) Steven Gerrard b) Gareth Barry c) Wayne Rooney
   d) Frank Lampard

3. Jose Mourinho was sacked after a 3-1 defeat to which team?
   a) Manchester City b) West Ham United c) Liverpool d) Everton

4. Where were they in the table when Mourinho was sacked?
   a) 12th b) 10th c) 8th d) 6th

5. His replacement Ole Gunnar Solskjaer went unbeaten in how many matches at the start of his tenure?
   a) 10 b) 11 c) 14 d) 15

6. Solskjaer's first game in charge was a 5-1 win against which club that he used to manage?
   a) Crystal Palace b) Bournemouth c) Cardiff City
   d) Huddersfield Town

7. United were knocked out of the Champions League 4-0 on aggregate by which team?
   a) Barcelona b) Paris Saint-Germain c) Juventus d) Bayern Munich

8. Manchester United won how many of their last nine league matches as they ended the campaign in sixth?
   a) 1 b) 2 c) 3 d) 4

9. How many league wins did they record against the other members of the so-called Big Six?
   a) 0 b) 1 c) 2 d) 3

10. With 16 goals in all competitions, who was United's top scorer?
    a) Romelu Lukaku b) Paul Pogba c) Anthony Martial
    d) Marcus Rashford

Answers: Page 231

2019-20

1. Manchester United played a pre-season friendly against Ole Gunnar Solskjaer's hometown club. Who are they?
   a) Kristiansund b) Molde c) Sandefjord d) Sarpsborg

2. Summer signing Daniel James arrived from which club?
   a) Bristol City b) Millwall c) Middlesbrough d) Swansea City

3. Bruno Fernandes helped turn United's season around after he arrived in January from which club?
   a) Porto b) Boavista c) Sporting Clube d) Benfica

4. In the Europa League, United became the first English team to play a competitive match in which country?
   a) Azerbaijan b) Gibraltar c) Armenia d) Kazakhstan

5. Odion Ighalo scored five goals on loan from which club?
   a) Watford b) Shanghai Shenhua c) Al-Shabab d) Udinese

6. United's last match before all sport was halted halted was against whom?
   a) LASK Linz b) Manchester City c) Norwich City
   d) Tottenham Hotspur

7.
   With the season interrupted by the Covid-19 pandemic, the latter stages of the Europa League were played over one leg at neutral venues. Where did United play their quarter and semi-finals?
   a) Porto b) Vienna c) Copenhagen d) Cologne

8. Due to the pandemic, what was the date of United's final league fixture?
   a) 30th June b) 12th July c) 26th July d) 5th August

9. At what stage did United exit the FA Cup, League Cup and Europa League?
   a) Last 16 b) Quarter-finals c) Semi-finals d) Final

10. United finished third, but how many points did they finish behind champions Liverpool?
    a) 21 b) 25 c) 29 d) 33

Answers: Page 231

FUN FACTS, STORIES AND STATS

1. At the end of the 2012-13 season, Sir Alex Ferguson retired as manager of Manchester United after 1500 games in charge. His final match was a 5-5 draw against West Bromwich Albion. He left having won United's 20th League title. The goal he set for himself when he joined the club 27 years earlier. To have consistently achieved what he did at the highest level of football makes him undeniably the greatest manager of all time.

2. Finding a successor to Sir Alex Ferguson was always going to be challenging. Which is why he decided to hand-pick the man himself. After 11 years in charge at Everton fellow Scot David Moyes took charge at Old Trafford. After his appointment a banner saying "The Chosen One" was displayed at Old Trafford. However, things did not go well for Moyes and he was eventually fired after 10 months in charge.

3. After Moyes left in April 2014, Ryan Giggs took over as the club's interim player-manager. He managed two wins, a draw and a defeat in the final four games of the 2013-14 season.

4. In the summer of 2014, after having guided his native Netherlands to the semi-finals of the World Cup in Brazil, Louis van Gaal became the club's first non-British manager.

5. In 2016 Louis van Gaal won their first trophy since Sir Alex Ferguson's departure by winning the FA Cup. They beat Crstal Palace 2-1 after extra time. Substitute Jesse lingard scoring the winner.

6. Forty-eight hours after his club lifted the FA Cupl at Wembley, van Gaal left Manchester United. A week later Jose Mourinho became manager. In his first competitive game for the club he won his first trophy, when he lifted the community shield after a 2-1 win against Leicester City at Wembely.

7. Mouinho brought in some exciting players like Zlatan Ibrahmovic and record signing Paul Pogba who returned for his second spell at the club having risen through the youth system but only managing seven appearances in 2011-12 before being sold to Juventus.

8. Mournho's first full season in charge was a successful one as he won the League Cup, after Zlatan Ibrahmovic's last minute winner against Southapmton at Wembley, and a Europa League triumph over Ajax in Stockholm.

9. After a poor start to the 2018/19 season Mourinho left the club and was replaced by Ole Gunnar Solskjaer, who was initially appointed as caretaker manager, but took the job full time shortly after

10. In the 2019-20 season Ole Gunnar Solskjaer appointed Ashley Young as club captain after Antonio Valencia's departure. However after Young's departure to Inter Milan in January 2020, Harry Maguire became the clubs captain.

TRIVIA QUIZ ANSWERS
Chapter 19: The Premier League Era - 2010's

2010-11
1. c) Guadalajara
2. d) Blackburn Rovers
3. d) 5th February
4. d) Bebe
5. a) Gary Neville
6. c) Manchester City
7. d) Blackburn Rovers
8. a) Schalke 04
9. b) Last 16
10. d) Wembley Stadium

2011-12
1. c) 8–2
2. d) Darren Fletcher
3. a) Romania
4. c) Athletic Bilbao
5. b) Paul Pogba
6. d) Paul Scholes
7. b) Sunderland
8. b) +56
9. a) 12
10. a) Nani

2012-13
1. a) Borussia Dortmund
2. b) The Manchester cotton industry
3. a) Nick Powell
4. b) Wilfried Zaha
5. c) Cristiano Ronaldo
6. d) Chelsea
7. a) Robin van Persie
8. c) 30
9. b) Swansea City
10. d) 5–5

2013-14
1. c) 11
2. d) Guillermo Varela
3. a) Wigan Athletic
4. b) Adnan Januzaj
5. a) Juan Mata
6. d) Olympiacos
7. d) Sunderland
8. b) 12
9. c) Everton
10. d) Norwich City

2014-15
1. b) 3rd
2. d) 1972
3. b) 4
4. d) Real Madrid
5. d) Milton Keynes Dons
6. a) 4
7. a) Arsenal
8. b) Cambridge United
9. a) 12
10. b) 4th

2015-16
1. d) PSV Eindhoven
2. b) Louis van Gaal's Army
3. c) Club Brugge
4. d) Liverpool
5. a) Marcus Rashford
6. b) Anthony Martial
7. d) Jesse Lingard
8. c) He was sacked
9. a) David de Gea
10. d) Angel di Maria

2016-17

1. d) Chelsea
2. b) £89m
3. d) Armenia
4. b) Zlatan Ibrahimovic
5. b) Tottenham Hotspur
6. d) 28
7. d) Twente
8. b) Stockholm
9. d) Henrikh Mkhitaryan
10. d) 6th

2017-18

1. d) Skopje, North Macedonia
2. b) Huddersfield Town
3. d) Chris Smalling
4. b) Finishing second
5. d) 19
6. d) Tottenham Hotspur
7. a) Chelsea
8. c) 18
9. c) 27
10. d) Michael Carrick

2018-19

1. b) Shakhtar Donetsk
2. d) Frank Lampard
3. c) Liverpool
4. d) 6th
5. b) 11
6. c) Cardiff City
7. a) Barcelona
8. b) 2
9. b) 1
10. b) Paul Pogba

2019-20

1. a) Kristiansund
2. d) Swansea City
3. c) Sporting Clube
4. d) Kazakhstan
5. b) Shanghai Shenhua
6. a) LASK Linz
7. d) Cologne
8. c) 26th July
9. c) Semi-finals
10. d) 33

Chapter 20

THE PREMIER LEAGUE ERA
2020's

2020-21

1. **Joining from Ajax, who was United's first signing of the season?**
   a) Anthony Elanga b) Alex Telles c) Timothy Fosu-Mensah
   d) Donny van der Beek

2. **Edinson Cavani arrived as a free agent after playing for which club?**
   a) Napoli b) Palermo c) Paris Saint-Germain d) Marseille

3. **PSG, RB Leipzig and which other team made up United's Champions League group?**
   a) İstanbul Başakşehir b) Trabzonspor c) Bursaspor d) Beşiktaş

4. **Who was the only player to score twice in Manchester United's 9-0 win over Southampton?**
   a) Edinson Cavani b) Scott McTominay c) Fred d) Anthony Martial

5. **United suffered their fourth semi-final exit under Solskjaer in the League Cup to which club?**
   a) Liverpool b) Manchester City c) Tottenham Hotspur d) Chelsea

6. **With 74 points, where did United finish in the league?**
   a) 2nd b) 3rd c) 4th d) 5th

7. **All five of United's Europa League opponents were either from Spain or which other country?**
   a) Italy b) France c) Germany d) Netherlands

8. **How many matches in all competitions were played in front of a crowd as Covid-19 restrictions continued?**
   a) 3 b) 9 c) 13 d) 19

9. **What was the score in the penalty shootout as United lost the Europa League final to Villarreal?**
   a) 9-8 b) 10-9 c) 11-10 d) 12-11

10. **Who finished as topscorer and won the Sir Matt Busby Player of the Year award?**
    a) Anthony Martial b) Marcus Rashford c) Edinson Cavani
    d) Bruno Fernandes

Answers: Page 239

2021-22

1. **Who was Manchester United's most expensive summer signing?**
   a) Tom Heaton b) Cristiano Ronaldo c) Jadon Sancho
   d) Raphael Varane

2. **Who did United beat 5-1 on the opening day of the season, their biggest win of the campaign?**
   a) Leeds United b) Watford c) Southampton d) Leicester City

3. **Cristiano Ronaldo scored twice against which team on his second debut for Manchester United?**
   a) Everton b) Wolverhampton Wanderers c) Newcastle United
   d) West Ham United

4. **Ronaldo on 24 goals and who on 10 were the only players to hit double figures in all competitions?**
   a) Marcus Rashford b) Jadon Sancho c) Edinson Cavani
   d) Bruno Fernandes

5. **Which former player was unbeaten as caretaker manager after Ole Gunnar Solskjaer was sacked?**
   a) Michael Carrick b) Paul Scholes c) Ryan Giggs d) Wayne Rooney

6. **United's only win in either domestic cup came against whom?**
   a) Sunderland b) Aston Villa c) West Ham United
   d) Wolverhampton Wanderers

7. **Which Spanish club put an end to United's Champions League hopes in the last 16?**
   a) Real Madrid b) Sevilla c) Barcelona d) Atletico Madrid

8. **Who became United's youngest Champions League goalscorer in that game?**
   a) Daniel James b) Anthony Elanga c) Hannibal Mejbri
   d) Alejandro Garnacho

9. **How many of Ralf Rangnick's 31 matches in charge did United win?**
   a) 11 b) 13 c) 15 d) 17

10. **58 points was United's lowest total in a league season since when?**
    a) 1994-95 b) 1989-90 c) 1986-87 d) 1978-79

Answers: Page 239

2022/23

1. David De Gea kept a clean sheet in the League Cup final against Newcastle in February 2023, breaking the club record of how many held by Peter Schmeichel?
   a) 160 b) 170 c) 180 d) 190

2. After 11 years at the club, Jesse Lingard left to join which club?
   a) Everton b) Nottingham Forest c) Leeds United d) Bournmouth

3. Uruguayan Edison Cavani left in the summer to join which club?
   a) Valencia b) Real Betis c) Villarreal d) Cadiz

4. How many Spanish teams did United face this season?
   a) 1 b) 2 c) 3 d) 4

5. Brazillian Antony signed from which club?
   a) Ajax b) AZ Alkmaar c) Feyenoord d) Twente

6. Erik Ten Hag's first competitive win was against which team?
   a) Arsenal b) Liverpool c) Everton d) Southampton

7. United played 10 domestic cup matches. How many did they win?
   a) 7 b) 8 c) 9 d) 10

8. United played 10 European matches. How many did they win?
   a) 7 b) 8 c) 9 d) 10

9. Who did United beat 2-0 in the League Cup final?
   a) Arsenal b) Man City c) Newcastle d) Chelsea

10. Marcus Rashford was the club's top scorer with 30 goals. Who was second with 14?
    a) Fred b) Bruno Fernandes c) Antony d) Casemiro

Answers: Page 239

FUN FACTS, STORIES AND STATS

1. On 18th April 2021, Manchester United announced they were joining 11 other European clubs as founding members of the Super League, a 20-team competition that would rival the current Champions League. After the announcement, there was a huge backlash from both United supporters and those of other clubs, from sponsors, media partners, players and the UK Government. The feeling amongst the football community was that it would negatively and unfairly affect the competitive nature of the football pyramid structure. The club withdraw just two days later.

2. The failure of the Super League project led to the executive vice-chairman Ed Woodward resigning from the club. There were huge protests against Woodward and the owners, the Glazer family which led to a pitch invasion ahead of a league match against Liverpool. The invasion led to the first postponement of a Premier League due to supporter protests in the competition's history.

3. United equalled the record biggest win in Premier League history when they destroyed Southampton 9-0 at Old Trafford on 2nd February 2021. There were eight different scorers that day.

4. United finished second in the 2020-21 Premier League season, which is their joint-highest finish since the retirement of Sir Alex Ferguson back in 2013. They finished 12 points behind Manchester City.

5. United reached the final of the 2021 Europa League where they faced Spanish side Villarreal. The match finished 1-1 in normal time and after neither side couldn't find a winner in extra time, the game went to a penalty shootout. Incredibly every outfield player scored their spot kick making the score 10-10 and meaning that the goalkeepers would take penalties themselves. Villarreal's keeper Gerónimo Rulli scored his penalty and then dramatically saved the shot from David De Gea, winning the trophy for the Spanish side.

6. In August 2021, Cristiano Ronaldo signed from Juventus after 12 years away from the club. He made an immediate impact, scoring 2 goals on his second debut against Newcastle United.

7. United finished 6th in the 2021-22 season meaning they did not qualify for the Champions League for the first time in three seasons. It was a disappointing season all round having been knocked out of the FA Cup on penalties to Middlesbrough, The third round of the League cup to West Ham United and in the first knockout stage of the Champions League to Atlético Madrid. This was the club's fifth season in a row without a trophy, which is their longest since a run of six between 1968–69 and 1973-74.

8. Manager Ole Gunnar Solskjær was sacked on 21st November 2021, and replaced by Michael Carrick. Then eight days later, Ralf Rangnick became interim manager until the end of the season. On 21st April former Ajax manager Erik ten Hag became the club's permanent

9. United won their sixth League Cup trophy against Newcastle United on 26th February 2023. The club's first silverware since 2017. Casemiro scored the opening and Marcus Rashford scored the second. David de Gea kept his 181st clean sheet for the club that day beating the record held by Peter Schmeichel.

10. The first-ever domestic Cup final to feature both Manchester sides took place on 3rd June 2023 at Wembley Stadium. It was the 190th competitive meeting between the two sides. Manchester City's captain İlkay Gündoğan scored after 15 seconds with the fastest-ever goal in an FA Cup final. City went on to win the match 2-1. Meaning United have won 78, City have won 59 and the remaining 53 games have been draws.

TRIVIA QUIZ ANSWERS
Chapter 20: The Premier League Era - 2020's

2020-21

1. d) Donny van der Beek
2. c) Paris Saint-Germain
3. a) İstanbul Başakşehir
4. d) Anthony Martial
5. b) Manchester City
6. a) 2nd
7. a) Italy
8. b) 9
9. c) 11-10
10. d) Bruno Fernandes

2021-22

1. c) Jadon Sancho
2. a) Leeds United
3. c) Newcastle United
4. d) Bruno Fernandes
5. a) Michael Carrick
6. b) Aston Villa
7. d) Atletico Madrid
8. b) Anthony Elanga
9. a) 11
10. b) 1989-90

2022-23

1. c) 180
2. b) Nottingham Forest
3. a) Valencia
4. d) 4
5. a) Ajax
6. b) Liverpool
7. d) 10
8. b) 8
9. c) Newcastle
10. b) Bruno Fernandes

THANK YOU FROM US

Thank you so much for reading the book.

You're in a great position to win a debate with anyone now!

Leaving a review will help other passionate fans expand their knowledge of the club and it will help us continue to create the highest quality books possible.

So if you enjoyed the book we'd be thankful if you could take a moment to help your fellow fans, and the team at Beautiful Games.

It will only take about 60 seconds and won't cost anything.

Simply scan this QR code:

Thank you so much for your help!

Glory Glory Man United!

Printed in Great Britain
by Amazon

35097076R00136